Introduction to Quality Assurance

Fred Tickle BA, CEng, M1MechE, MIEE, MIQA
and
Geoff Vorley MSc, MIQA

Founding Directors of Quality Management & Training Limited
Associate Lecturers at University of Surrey

Fred Tickle

Geoff Vorley

Quality Management & Training (Publications) Limited
PO Box 172
Guildford
Surrey
GU2 6AL
Telephone/Fax: +44 -(0) 1483 453511/2
E-Mail: denise@qmt.co.uk
Web Site: http:\\www.cableol.co.uk\qmt\index.htm

Quality Management & Training (Publications) Limited
PO Box 172, Guildford, Surrey, GU2 6AL

First Published by Quality Management & Training (Publications) Limited 1998

British Library Cataloguing in publications data

A catalogue record for this book is available from the British Library

ISBN   0 9528391 1 3

Printed and Bound in Great Britain by :
Biddles Limited
Woodbridge Park Estate, Woodbridge Road, Guildford, Surrey GU1 1DA

Introduction to Quality Assurance

Introduction to the Book

The aim of this book is to provide an understanding of the principles of quality assurance. The book will explain the way in which these quality assurance principles relate and can be applied to the design, development, manufacture and delivery of products and services. The object being to enhance the reader's awareness of Quality Assurance and its terminology and bring the subject alive sufficiently to encourage and motivative for quality assurance. Statistical methods are a vital part of any Quality Assurance or Total Quality Management initiative and it is for this reason a practical approach has been adopted in the explanation of this important topic. Information is provided by practical example of the application of statistics in the quality environment.

The book covers the Institute of Quality Assurance (IQA) A11 syllabus and is of obvious application for students participating in the IQA A11 examination. As a result of adhering to the requirements of the IQA A11 syllabus, the book's content reflects the current thinking of the IQA, in terms of the latest key quality issues facing Directors, Managers and Technicians. The book provides a clear approaches and examples of how to respond to these key quality issues.

There is naturally and correctly some overlap with the accompanying sister publication, *Quality Management (Principles & Techniques)*, as certain explanations would not be clear.

The book is divided into three parts, below is an outline of the contents of each section and what could reasonably expected to be appreciated having studied each section.

Introduction to Quality Assurance

PART A

The Need for Quality Assurance and Quality Control.

The Concept of Quality and its Control.
This section is intended to provide sufficient information to:
- understand the concepts of quality and its control and various definitions associated with quality and reliability,
- ability to establishment and interpret company quality policy,
- understand the concept of total involvement in quality assurance and importance of communication and feedback of information,
- justify quality assurance activities with regard to commercial, legal responsibilities and cost reduction.

Standards and Specifications.
This section is intended to provide sufficient information to:
- describe the need, importance and application of specifications and standardisation in the quality control system,
- prepare specifications for purposes of testing a product or service,
- use a product or service specification as a basis for a contract or conducting an external audit,
- determine from the product or service specification the process measurement criteria (Process Capability Studies),
- determine the ability of the process to meet specification (Process Capability Studies),
- understand the relationship between specifications, measurements and process capabilities.

Natural, Material and Subjective Standards.
This section is intended to provide sufficient information to:
- understand natural, material and subjective standards and their applicability, develop and create a calibration system,
- understand the concepts of traceability and hierarchy in connection with inspection and testing measuring equipment.

Standards and Standardising Organisations.

This section is intended to provide sufficient information to:

- describe the roles and responsibilities of the various standardising organisations (company, industrial, national and international) and the importance of international standards harmonisation,
- understand and complete the process or procedure for obtaining product certification including a third party.

Cost of Quality.

This section is intended to provide sufficient information to:

- complete a quality cost analysis of the prevention, appraisal and failure costs associated with an organisation.

PART B

Design for Quality.

This section is intended to provide sufficient information to:

- understand the concept of value and economics in design quality, specifications and tolerancing,
- use specifications as an essential part of communication,
- understand the purpose of standards specification and the role of BSI and ISO,
- ensure an effective contribution of the quality assurance department during design and development; prototype testing, field trials phases of a design project,
- understand how to complete a hazard assessment, failure mode and effect and criticality analysis,
- understand how to complete an analysis of tolerance requirements and a statistical analysis of tolerancing,
- prepare quality control schemes and their documentation,
- control specification amendment and implement a concession procedure,
- rationalise product ranges and use preferred numbers and variety reduction,
- understand the need and application of design codes of practice and design guides.

Reliability.

This section is intended to provide sufficient information to:

- be able to define reliability, with specific regard to BS 4778,

- interpret lifetime distributions in terms of probability density function and reliability function,
- understand the basic concepts of simple series and parallel systems and the use of redundancy to improve reliability.

PART C

Control of Supplies.
This section is intended to provide sufficient information to:
- control the process of procuring bought-in goods and services,
- complete a supplier evaluation and vendor rating,
- organise and document purchasing and sub-contracting procedures,
- control quarantine and bonded stores .

Quality Control of Processes.
This section is intended to provide sufficient information to:
- use process capability analysis to understand the ability of the process to meet the quality requirements,
- identify and establish a quality control strategy and inspection procedures (e.g. 1st - off, last - off, patrol inspection, choice of inspection stages, etc.),
- understand the responsibilities to the customer for final inspection and test,
- create batch identification procedures for safety-critical products,
- understand the need for protective packaging.

Inspection of Processes.
This section is intended to provide sufficient information to:
- establish and create inspection procedures,
- determine the factors influencing the choice of 100% inspection versus sampling, variables versus attributes etc.,
- establish, create and implement procedures for dealing with defective supplies,
- understand the application of automatic inspection methods,
- understand how computers can be used for data handling and process control,
- understand the Quality Control issues and problems associated with high/low volume throughput processes.

PART D

Basic Statistical Methods.
This section is intended to provide sufficient information to:
- understand the concept of variability when applied to continuous and discrete random variables,
- calculate binomial and poisson distributions,
- apply acceptance sampling by attributes,
- construct operating characteristics curve for a single sampling plan,
- interpret the implications of an operating characteristic curve and understand the risks involved in sampling,
- calculate probability distributions for continuous random variables,
- calculate and establish normal distribution and explain the reasons for widespread use of normal distribution to model production and service processes,
- understand the basic ideas of control charts and compile control charts for means and ranges of measured variables and number defective and proportion defective,
- calculation and use of decision lines on control charts,
- understand, calculate and apply cusum charts.

*The book was intended to be written in a way that hopefully makes the various techniques and approaches to Quality Assurance self explanatory. However, if the reader has any problems with the contents or has a quality problem or issue that they would like to discuss further, please do not hesitate in contacting Fred or Geoff. We can be contacted via the publishers - **we welcome the opportunity to discuss quality issues**.*

This book could not have been completed without the invaluable contribution provided by Denise Grant (BA Hons).

PART A

The Need for Quality Assurance and Control

The Need for Quality Assurance

Why Quality Assurance Is So Important

There are any number of imperatives associated with quality assurance. Detailed below are what are considered to be the more important, namely:

Economic - The cost of poor quality and the opportunity for significant cost savings,
Legal - The law associated with Quality Assurance both criminal and civil,
Marketing - The competition and customer satisfaction,
Survival - We live in a dangerous world. Can Quality Assurance provide some protection?

The Economic Imperative

Figure 1 illustrates the consequential cost of errors or changes introduced at various stages of the product cycle:

If an error is made at the sales stage and is discovered and corrected immediately, then the cost of the error is limited to the cost of re-working the sales process. If the error is not discovered until after the design stage, then the cost of the error

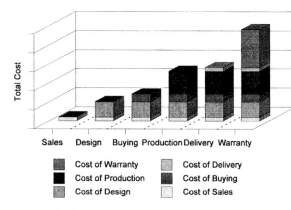

Figure 1 Cost of errors

includes not only re-working the sales process but also the design process. And so it goes on. If the error is not discovered until after delivery, then the costs to rectify the error may be enormous.

Introduction to Quality Assurance

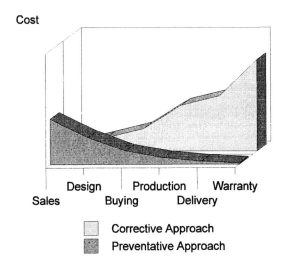

Cost

Design | Production | Warranty
Sales | Buying | Delivery

Corrective Approach
Preventative Approach

Figure 2 Benefits of Investing in Prevention

Figure 2 illustrates the importance of preventing errors as early as possible. For this reason, the Japanese have turned the graph around and invest money at the front end to ensure that design errors are not fed into the cycle. This investment is far less than the costs of correction resulting from not investing.

The Legal Imperative

There are numerous examples of organisations being fined as a result of poor quality of products or services. Strict laws are now in place in the UK to protect the consumer, e.g. the Strict Liability law specifies that the immediate supplier of a product or service is liable for it being of satisfactory quality. The retailer cannot hide behind the fact that their supplier is to blame.

The Marketing Imperative

Unless an organisation is in a virtually monopolistic situation, it is going to have to watch its competitors very carefully to ensure that it can retain market share. The Japanese have demonstrated that quality and reliability sells. Their success can no longer be attributed to cheap labour costs but rather to the efficiency with which they have re-engineered products to be more reliable and cheaper.

Consider a company which has the lion's share of the market, say 30%. If its quality record is at the same level as its nearest competitor, company B, which has, say 10% of the market, then in real terms A has three times the number of disappointed customers as B. Everyone knows someone who has a defective product from A. In other words, A has three times the exposure and must, therefore, be at least three times better.

The car industry provides good examples of this. Vauxhall in the mid 50's nearly went out of business; Lancia in the 80's lost most of their UK markets; Jaguar in the 70's and Rovers in the early 80's likewise.

The Need For Quality Assurance

The Survival Imperative

Today, as never before, society is virtually totally dependent on technology and quality failures frequently have catastrophic consequences.

You only have to read the newspapers to begin to realise the world is a very dangerous place!

"Holiday jet battered by barrage of bricks

A holiday jet carrying 145 passengers was seriously damaged by flying bricks as it took off from Luton airport last week. Thrust from the engine lifted paving slabs from the runway, throwing them up to strike tail stabiliser, causing damage."

"Wrong bolts held aircraft windscreen

The windscreen of the British Airways BAC 1-11 airliner which blew out at 17,000 feet, sucking the captain half out of the cockpit was held in with the wrong bolts."

"Wiring technician made mistakes all his working life

'Positively dangerous' working practices which caused the Clapham Junction rail disaster in which 35 people died."
The report on the disaster revealed negligence at eleven levels of supervision and management.

"GPs' sloppy handwriting 'still killing patients'

Inderal - for controlling high blood pressure - was mistaken for the asthma agent Intal. The patient died. An anaesthetics registrar injected what he thought was atropine - used before operations - and the patient had a fatal heart attack. The ampoule had contained adrenaline."

"Bolt Change caused Chinook crash

A comparatively minor design change introduced last year caused a vital gearbox component to fail catastrophically. Forty-five men died in the crash."

This small selection should leave us in no doubt about the importance of Quality Assurance as we enter the new millennium.

Introduction to Quality Assurance

The Quality Concept

Quality is the totality of features and characteristics of a product or service that bear on its ability to satisfy a given need (BS 4778/ISO 8402).

When asked to name a quality pen most people respond with names such as Parker, Schaefer, Mont Blanc, Cross or Waterman. Occasionally, someone suggests Bic. This obvious contrast reveals misconceptions about the word 'quality'.

I am sure that the quality manager of Bic would consider that his pens are of high quality just as much as those of other manufacturers.

There is clearly a difference between, say, a Parker pen and a Bic pen but it is not quality.

In simple terms, quality means Fitness for Purpose or, 'to satisfy a given need'.

Compare the expectations for a Bic pen with those for a Parker and it can be seen that they serve different purposes. The Bic pen is considered to be merely a writing tool while the Parker pen is expected to serve the additional purpose of being a prestigious gift. Consequently, the Parker pen will have many more features and characteristics to satisfy its purpose.

Needs cover more than mere function. Many factors affect the ability of a product or service to satisfy needs.

Needs include:
- availability;
- appearance;
- method of distribution;
- initial cost;
- running costs;
- user awareness or knowledge;
- other possible uses including reasonable misuse (e.g. using a screw driver to open a tin of paint or a chair to stand on);
- expected life;
- storage requirements;
- service requirements;
- interaction with other items when used;
- whether it is user friendly

13

The Need For Quality Assurance

Needs also must include what the product must not do.
- Bombs must not explode until required to do so.
- Products must not cause:
    - injury
    - a threat to health
    - a safety hazard
    - damage to the environment
- And they must not do this:
    - when they are working
    - when they are not working
    - when they are being repaired or serviced
    - when they fail
    - when they are being disposed of

Quality versus grade

Quality is the degree to which the customers' expectations are met. If the Bic pen meets all of its expectations then it is of high quality. Similarly, a Parker pen which did not meet all of its expectations would be a low quality pen. Quality is, therefore, independent of price; it is related to expectations.

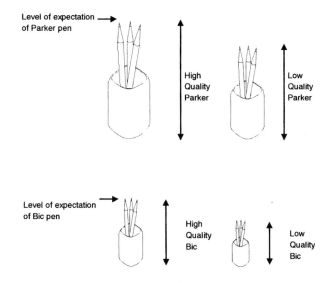

Figure 3

As stated above, clearly there is a difference but it is not quality. ISO 8402 defines this difference in expectations as the GRADE of the product or service.

Introduction to Quality Assurance

Quality should not be confused with Grade. Grade is the extent of features and characteristics offered for a given price. Grade is a function of price. A higher grade demands a higher price. Consumers choose the grade according to their pocket coupled with their expectations. Quality, on the other hand, is not a function of price.

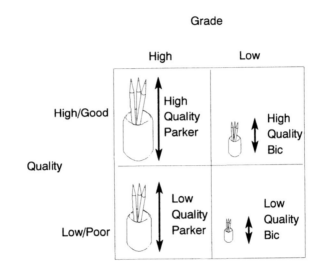

Figure 4

Consumers expect a high quality regardless of what they have paid - the product must satisfy their expectations.

The above distinction is particularly important in these days when public services are being contracted out. As the cost of public services becomes more competitive, there is a great danger that the lowering of quality can become confused with lowering of grade. Traditionally in the UK public services have evolved almost regardless of cost and, therefore, many features of services have become the expected norm. When the cost of these services has to be paid for directly, as opposed to a voted budget, questions are asked as to what is being paid for. This may lead to the pruning of services down to essential features. This should not be confused with the quality which should still be of the highest standard for the grade.

By way of illustration: eye surgery in the UK is still carried out in high grade, and consequently expensive, operating theatres. In Russia, a large proportion of eye surgery is now carried out on a travelling bus equipped with the minimum essential facilities with no compromise on the quality of the surgery.

This trend is likely to increase so it is vitally important that to avoid 'throwing away the baby with the bath water' a clear distinction is made between quality and grade.

The Need For Quality Assurance

Craftsmen and scientists have long traditions of producing the best that is possible. It is necessary to learn what it means to produce the best that is possible, albeit with reduced expectations as to the scope of features included in the product or service. Is it really the role of the hospital to provide staff with a bowling green and immaculate cricket pitch employing teams of groundsmen and gardeners? Patients are increasingly asking "what am I paying for?". These are emotive issues with political overtones which must not cloud over judgement when the customer decides what he is prepared to pay for and the price he is prepared to pay for it.

Quality of a product (manufacturing)

ISO 8402 defines quality as:

Quality is the totality of features and characteristics of a product or service that bear on its ability to satisfy a given need (BS 4778/ISO 8402).

The following diagram illustrates the relationship of various quality related terms:

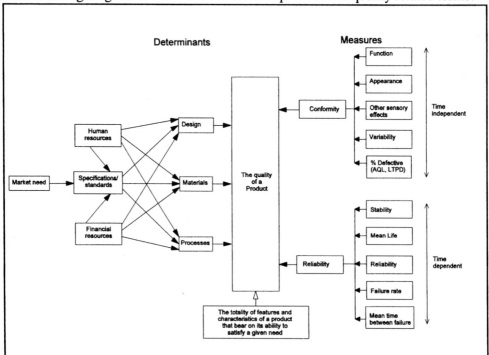

Figure 5

Introduction to Quality Assurance

Note: There are two measures of quality: conformity and reliability.

Conformity is determined by inspection and test.

Reliability is a probability of what happens in time under defined conditions and is indicated by MTBF (mean time between failure), failure rate, probability of successful operation, etc.

The determinants of quality

1. Quality of design

This is the degree to which the user's needs have been understood, translated into product or service specifications and communicated to subsequent departments. Marketing, sales or contract departments are usually responsible for ensuring that the users' needs are fully understood. While Clive Sinclair's C5 car was extremely well researched and designed, customer reaction was not tested prior to its launch with disastrous results. Currently, corned beef tins cause 11,500 reported casualties per year in the UK. Design departments are responsible for verifying the soundness of designs. When modifying the design of the Chinook helicopter propeller drive by increasing the size of a bolt, designers neglected to examine adequately the consequences of the reduced wall thickness caused by the increased hole size, again with disastrous results. Drawing offices are responsible for communicating design specifications in an unambiguous way. Drawings which specified that a two-part assembly should be tested to withstand 40N force did not specify a tolerance, with the result that the inspector applied 60N force "to be on the safe side" thus causing a potential weakness which may not be discovered until some time after delivery.

New Design Control includes the planning, techniques and documented procedures used to ensure that the customer's requirements are fully understood and interpreted into a practical and viable manufacturing specification, with due consideration for all performance, safety and reliability related requirements.

2. Quality of procurement

Purchasing and quality departments should be responsible for ensuring that the required quality is obtained for materials, components and sub-contract services which they are effectively purchasing on behalf of the customer. Many companies have suffered losses because they have "been let down by their suppliers". Companies cannot pass on the responsibility to their sub-contractors or suppliers. What they can do is to carry out sufficient assessments of suppliers to establish what confidence they can have with regard to the quality of their supplies or services before purchasing from them. During 1987, the USA government had to set up a senate enquiry into the extent of the potential risk resulting from the importation of nuts and bolts from unknown sources in the Far East; it was discovered that mild steel was being supplied as high strength alloy steel.

Purchasing Control includes all the techniques associated with ensuring that the quality of supplies consistently meet the specified requirements in terms of price, performance, delivery, service and quality.

3. *Quality of process*es

Quality of processes start with planning. Clearly, the method of manufacture must be economic but it is false economy, for instance, to leave inspection to the last stage which very often happens. It is usually going to cost more in the long run to correct any defects found at this stage. Starting a job without checking first of all that everything necessary to do the job is available appears to be stating the obvious but it is amazing how often this is the case. Using the wrong tools or make-do gauges, not checking the first-off, not monitoring the process for drift or deterioration of tool condition, taking short cuts, relying on instruments and controllers which have not been calibrated, mishandling, poor storage facilities are just some of the common causes of poor quality. Because a disconnected wire was not trimmed back or made secure during modifications, signals at Clapham Junction malfunctioned resulting in many deaths and injuries.

Process Control includes all the documented methods associated with ensuring that the product conforms to specified requirements including the subsequent stages, such as: packaging, installation and servicing.

Quality Control

The traditional approach towards quality (detection)

In the days when a craftsman saw the whole job through from start to finish, quality was synonymous with craftsmanship. The craftsman would ensure quality at every stage. The advent of Taylorism, Fordism, Work Study led to the division of labour, firstly between 'Planners' and 'Doers', and, secondly, between tasks themselves, de-skilling led, on the one hand, to a loss of personal involvement and a sense of pride in one's work, and a need for planning and co-ordination on the other. This resulted in the formation of centralised inspection departments and quality being controlled by filtering out defective work during inspection stages. It was reactive and detection orientated. It also tended to suggest that quality problems were related to the manufacturing process whereas studies on the origin of quality problems have shown that up to 60% of quality problems are design faults. If the traditional approach to controlling quality with the emphasis on monitoring the manufacturing or production process is employed. If there is a design error the best that can be achieved is to make the product perfectly wrong! Clearly there was a need to extend control of quality into other areas that could have an impact on the final quality of the product or service.

Traditional Inspection

Detection Oriented

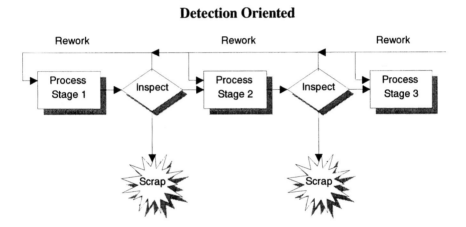

Inspection is used as a filter to sort good from bad
Continuous feedback of defective work for correction

Figure 6

Step 1   Set up machine
Step 2   Inspect first off
Step 3   If first off is OK then continue, otherwise re-set the machine until OK.
Step 4   On completion, transport goods to the inspection department to carry out
         100% inspection to sort the good from the bad.
Step 5   Scrap or re-work defectives.

The Need For Quality Assurance

There are a number of problems with this approach:

♦ Time, effort and energy are wasted on manufacturing defective products.
♦ Loss of manufacturing capacity carrying out re-work.
♦ Delivery delays and loss of profit or custom.
♦ 100% inspection does not necessarily mean 100% detection and, therefore, some defectives find their way to the customer.

Traditional inspection = DETECTION of out-of-limit parts = Waste

---

The modern approach towards quality (prevention)

The complexities in technology and integration of designs have made total quality control by inspection alone unsuitable. Inspection can only determine the quality of an item in the 'as-made' condition. To ensure reliability, which is the time-dependent dimension of quality, it is necessary to build-in quality at every stage. In recent years a new approach towards achieving quality and reliability has evolved known as the systems approach to Quality Assurance. Since every stage of the product or service cycle is a potential source of failure, it must be considered just what could go wrong at each stage. Quality is the degree to which this is successfully achieved for each of the above functions. It follows, therefore, that quality achievement must be planned. This implies the examination at each stage of the process and careful consideration of the potential deviations and the methods and techniques necessary to prevent the occurrence of defective work. Quality Assurance is pro-active rather than re-active.

Quality Control Approach

Prevention Orientated

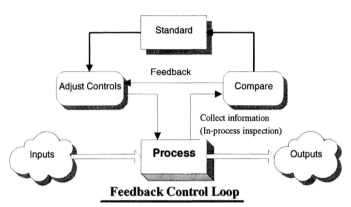

Inspection is used to collect information about the process
In-process inspection ensures timely prevention

Figure 7

Step 1. Start right

- Check that the operator, machine, tools etc. are capable with respect to the specified tolerance.
- Check instructions, drawings, documentation are available and at the right issue.
- Set up the machine.
- Inspect first off.
- If the first off is not within tolerance readjust machine and repeat until correct.

Step 2. Keep right

- Inspect samples at suitable intervals.
- Plot inspection results on control charts.
- Interpret control chart and take corrective action when necessary.

Step 3. Finish right

- Inspect last item and plot on chart.
- Complete records and return documentation.
- Protect components for transport to next stage.
- Return tools for refurbishment and safe storage.
- Carry out any planned maintenance.

Benefits of this approach:

Manufacture of defective items is avoided.
Defective work is prevented and, therefore, does not result in field failures.
Increased manufacturing efficiency and profitability.

> **Modern Techniques = PREVENTION of out-of limit parts**
> **= Savings/Benefits**

It is clearly more sensible to avoid waste and hold-ups by adopting a policy of
PREVENTION and **"Right First Time"**.

A. V. Feigenbaum - Total Quality Control

Feigenbaum is one of the gurus who helped the Japanese to understand and implement
Quality Control techniques in the 50's. Feigenbaum's book "Total Quality Control"
was originally written in 1951 but organisations in the West are only now employing
some of the concepts and principles embodied in his book. Total Quality Control, not
to be confused with Total Quality Management, may be considered to be the forerunner
to BS EN ISO9001 (1994). Feigenbaum's book is essentially a model for a Quality
Assurance Management System (like ISO 9000) rather than TQM which may be
considered more of a motivational concept.

Originally, quality assurance was mainly considered to be controlling the quality of
manufacture. Feigenbaum had the foresight to see that this was only part of the story.
Quality was Total and needed to involve all functions associated with the process of
fulfilling the customer requirements; from initial specification and design control
through to the manufacturing stages. More recently, this concept has been extended
vertically, into service industries and, horizontally, by encompassing all departments
within an organisation, with the introduction of the concept of 'internal customers'.

Introduction to Quality Assurance

One of the key elements of Feigenbaum's Total Quality Control message is the need for a co-ordinated and documented approach to controlling quality across the complete organisation. These documented procedures are the guide for the action of personnel throughout all of the process stages of delivering a product or service. The Total Quality Control approach to each of these process stages is shown in the diagram and explained below.

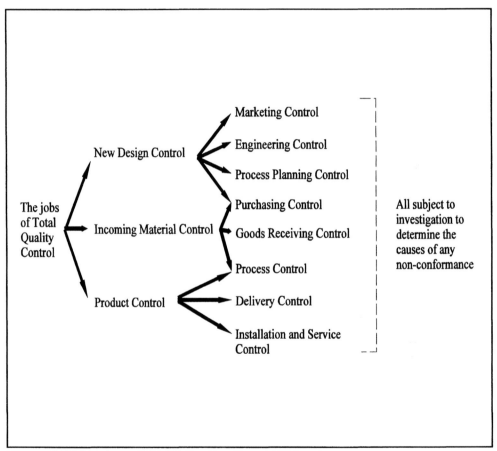

Figure 8 Feigenbaum's Total Quality Control Triangle
(Adapted from A. V. Feigenbaum's Total Quality Control)

The Need For Quality Assurance

Quality control model

Figure 9 describes a typical process from customer requirements, through design and development, purchase of materials, process control to delivery and subsequent service support.

The Quality Assurance system has in this case established the support activities that ensure that quality control activities are consistently and effectively implemented.

The right-hand side of the diagram indicates the

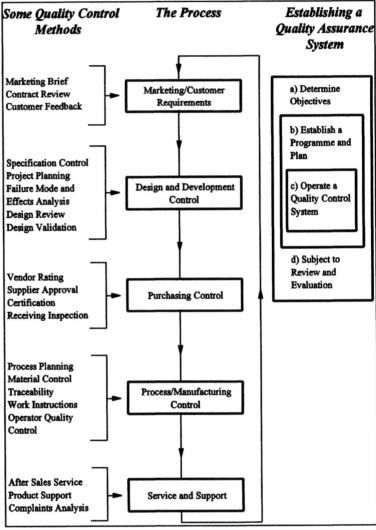

Some Quality Control Methods	The Process	Establishing a Quality Assurance System
Marketing Brief Contract Review Customer Feedback	Marketing/Customer Requirements	a) Determine Objectives
		b) Establish a Programme and Plan
Specification Control Project Planning Failure Mode and Effects Analysis Design Review Design Validation	Design and Development Control	c) Operate a Quality Control System
		d) Subject to Review and Evaluation
Vendor Rating Supplier Approval Certification Receiving Inspection	Purchasing Control	
Process Planning Material Control Traceability Work Instructions Operator Quality Control	Process/Manufacturing Control	
After Sales Service Product Support Complaints Analysis	Service and Support	

Figure 9 Quality Assurance Model
Adapted from BS4891

process of determining the quality system for each stage in the process:

a. Determine the objectives.
b. Institute a programme and plan to achieve the objectives.
c. Establish the quality control systems for each stage in the process.

d.   Review and evaluate the implementation of the applied quality controls.

The left-hand side of the diagram indicates some of the quality control methods that would be appropriate for regulating each stage. For example, at the design and development stage the quality control objectives include implementation of specification control, project planning, FMECA, design review and design validation. Note the list is not complete. There are numerous other quality control methods that can be employed.

The right-hand shows that to achieve these objectives:
(a) a programme or plan needs to be established (b) to enable the implementation of specification control, project planning, FMECA, design review and design validation. Operating the system (c) can then begin. However, there is a need to monitor such activities (d). For design control, specification control, project planning, FMECA, design review and design validation control would be normally monitored by means of review and evaluation (Audit).

Quality Assurance

Taylorism and Fordism

During the twentieth century, the intention of Taylorism and Fordism has been to minimise human error by transferring skills to machines reducing workers to mere doers who are not expected to think about the way things are done. Further separation of the responsibility for quality by the centralisation of inspection has left the average worker bereft of any personal involvement in the work. As a consequence, workers have become increasingly mercenary about work seeking financial compensation for the sheer monotony and boredom they experience in the workplace.

Job satisfaction

This trend came to a head in the 60's, particularly in the car industry. Furthermore, there was increasing evidence that the policy of treating workers as unthinking machine operatives and the effect this had on worker attitudes played a significant part in poor quality. Many schemes were devised in an attempt to counter these negative attitudes at work and increase job involvement. Schemes such as Job Awareness, Job Rotation, Job Enlargement, Job Enrichment were collectively known as Job Satisfaction schemes or Job Restructuring.

The Need For Quality Assurance

Japan

Meanwhile, Japan was being guided through a rapid transition from its non-threatening pre-industrial status to a threatening contender in the world market place by the Gurus Deming, Juran and Feigenbaum. However, having the benefit of hindsight, the Japanese avoided the extremes of Taylorism and Fordism. Instead they engaged the participation of the workers in the form of Quality Circles. By allowing small groups of workers to have regular meetings to learn how to solve problems, they discovered enormous achievements could be made in the form of savings and quality improvements.

Quality assurance today

Quality Assurance is about everyone being responsible for quality. It is an about-turn on the Fordist perception of the worker. The last thirty years have seen a new philosophy of management emerging in which the worker is seen as a key problem solver and the management as the resource. The current buzz word is 'empowerment'. Many middle managers see this as a threat to their authority and power. This is due to a misconception of the idea. Empowerment should not be seen as a diminishing of management's power but an unleashing of the worker's latent creative power hitherto denied.

According to traditional views of economics, countries having the most material resources would lead world markets. That is why so many wars have been fought over resource rich countries. It explains why pioneers were financed to extend the British Empire. It explains the concept of the Commonwealth. However, the Japanese at the end of the war, left with no natural resources, demonstrated the truth of the most valuable asset, which the West had denied. This was to recognise the potential of each individual human being. The traditional views have been challenged by this new approach and found wanting. We are now having to learn from the Japanese how to undo a century of non-involvement of workers.

The most common approach is the establishment of teams and the organisational adjustments necessary to develop teamwork. Workers are now being involved at all levels of decision-making in the organisation. Taylor's division of labour at the start of this century introduced the need for formal communication between the 'planners' and the 'doers'. At the close of this century as we move beyond the industrial age into the information age, new communication skills are needed to allow full participation while maintaining co-ordination and control. Accountability is being decentralised enabling local involvement in decision making. At the same time, everyone is perceived as part of an information loop known as the feedback system. For example, the role of inspection is no longer to detect defective work but to gather information about the process with a view to preventing defective work.

One thing is sure, competent and committed leadership is more important than ever. Managers can no longer separate their own behaviour from what they expect from others. That is why schemes such as ISO 9000 place so much emphasis on the Quality Policy Statement. Managers must be seen to 'walk the talk'.

A Documented Quality System

A Quality System is the organisational structure, responsibilities, procedures, processes and resources for implementing quality management. The quality system should only be as comprehensive as needed to meet the quality objectives. For contractual, mandatory and assessment purposes, demonstration of the implementation of identified elements in the system may be required.

An example of the importance of quality records - The USS Thresher

The accuracy of this story may not be exactly correct but it does convey the importance of quality systems and records.

The USS Thresher was an American nuclear submarine which sank with the loss of all crew. As a result there was a formal inquiry held to identify the possible causes of the disaster. The inquiry team comprised (amongst others) of the people responsible for what is now know as first level systems. i.e. those systems concerned with preventing submerging and surfacing of the submarine.

- The propulsion system (Propellers Steam turbines etc.)
- Ballast system (Pumps and air and hydraulics etc.)
- The control surfaces (rudder, hydroplanes, etc.)
- The power supply (Nuclear power plant)
- Pressure hull (The structure of the submarine)

The story goes that the Naval Officers associated with each of the above elements had assembled when Admiral Rickover walked in with a huge pile of records. "Good day gentlemen" he said " I have here all the quality records associated with the Threshers Nuclear power plant proving that my Nuclear system works satisfactorily. Where are your records to prove the same?" With that said, the Admiral walked out of the room. The truth of the above may be in doubt(but the point has still been well made i.e.- that the Nuclear Quality Assurance System was in place). Unfortunately the same rigeur was not in place for the submarine's other system (eg the engines). The other Officers could not prove (provide quality records) the quality of their systems. From this incident "First Level" was born. From this time onwards all systems which effect the submarines ability to submerge and surface were classified as First Level and therefore attract a higher standard of control (A Quality Assurance System Standard).

Introduction to Quality Assurance

Demonstration and documentation

Demonstration of the quality system refers to:

- the adequacy of the quality system (e.g. in design, production, installation and servicing),
- providing documented evidence that the prescribed system is operating effectively.

Documentation may include quality manuals, descriptions of quality related procedures, quality system auditing reports and other quality records. All documentation should be legible, dated (or status), clear, readily identifiable and maintained in an orderly manner.

Data may be hard-copy or stored electronically in a computer. In addition, the quality management system should provide a method for removing and/or disposing of documentation used in the manufacture of products when that documentation has become out-of-date. The following are examples of the types of documents requiring control:

- drawings
- specifications
- inspection instructions
- test procedures
- work instructions
- operation sheets
- quality manual
- operational procedures
- quality assurance procedures

The system should also require that sufficient records be maintained to demonstrate achievement of the required quality and verify effective operation of the quality management system. The following are examples of quality records requiring control:

- contract reviews
- list of suppliers and subcontractors
- inspection reports
- test data
- certificates of conformity
- audit reports

A Documented Quality System

- calibration data
- customer complaints
- training

Quality records should be retained for a specified period, in such a manner as to be retrievable for analysis in order to identify quality trends and the need for, and effectiveness of, corrective action. Whilst in storage, quality records should be protected from damage, loss and deterioration due to environmental conditions.

Quality system documentation structure

The Quality System documentation is usually structured into three levels as follows:

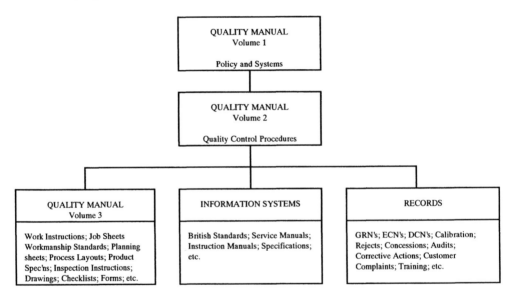

Volume 1 of the Quality Manual provides an overview of the Company's Quality System and the Company's policy with respect to the requirements of ISO 9001, 9002 or 9003.

Volume 2 of the Quality Manual provides a more detailed description of the overall procedures and responsibilities for operating the Quality System.

The documentation at level three is divided into three:

a) documentation which is specific to customers orders, and instructs employees on the correct sequence to perform various tasks.

b) general information and data such as specifications and standards.

c) records which demonstrate the operation of the quality system and provide the basis for analysis and corrective actions.

Management commitment - The quality policy statement

The Quality Policy Statement is a company's statement of intent with regard to the quality of the goods or services provided to their customers. This statement is usually found in the front of the Quality Manual and posted throughout the company..

Purpose of the quality policy statement

- To provide the customer with the confidence that the company is going to supply good products or services and that they have made a commitment to quality.
- To indicate to the employees that the company's management has given the 'stamp of authority' to the commitment to quality.

A Documented Quality System

Contents of quality policy statement

Quality Policy Statements are often found to contain the following:

- Reference to satisfying the customer's requirements.
- Reference to the commitment to effective management and cost effective products or services.
- Statement that compliance with the contents of the Quality Manual and associated procedures is a mandatory requirement on all employees.
- Signature at the end of the policy statement by the chief executive of the company endorsing the commitment.

QUALITY POLICY STATEMENT

Quality Management and Training Limited is proud of its reputation for providing consultancy and training services in the field of quality assurance. To ensure that this reputation continues and that clients can remain confident of the quality of our service, we have implemented management systems which meet the requirements of ISO 9001.

To this end, all activities affecting the processes of consultancy and training are controlled by procedures which are defined in a Quality Manual. These procedures, while not restricting the flair and experience of the consultants, ensure that essential tasks are controlled and checked for accuracy.

It is, therefore, a requirement on all personnel in the organisation to comply with the procedures laid down in the Quality Manual and the associated work instructions which are issued with my full approval and commitment.

(Signed)

Managing Director.

Introduction to Quality Assurance

Interpreting the Quality Policy Statement

No matter how well intentioned, it is easy for a Quality Policy Statement to become fine words without any real effect on how the company operates and without it being possible to check whether it is being fulfilled. It is essential, therefore, that the company makes it quite clear how the Quality Policy Statement is to be interpreted. This can take various forms:

- The statement often needs to be translated into language which is more appropriate for the local work - a production line, a purchasing office, a design group, and so on.
- ISO 9001 requires companies to translate the quality policy into specific objectives. This allows the company to check how well its policy is being realised more exactly.
- Review by management at board meetings.

The Quality Hierarchy

Quality assurance: All those planned and systematic actions necessary to provide adequate confidence that a product or service will satisfy given requirements for quality.

Quality control: The operational techniques and activities that are used to fulfil requirements for quality.

Inspection: Activities such as measuring, examining, testing, gauging one or more characteristics of a product or service and comparing these with specified requirements to determine conformity.

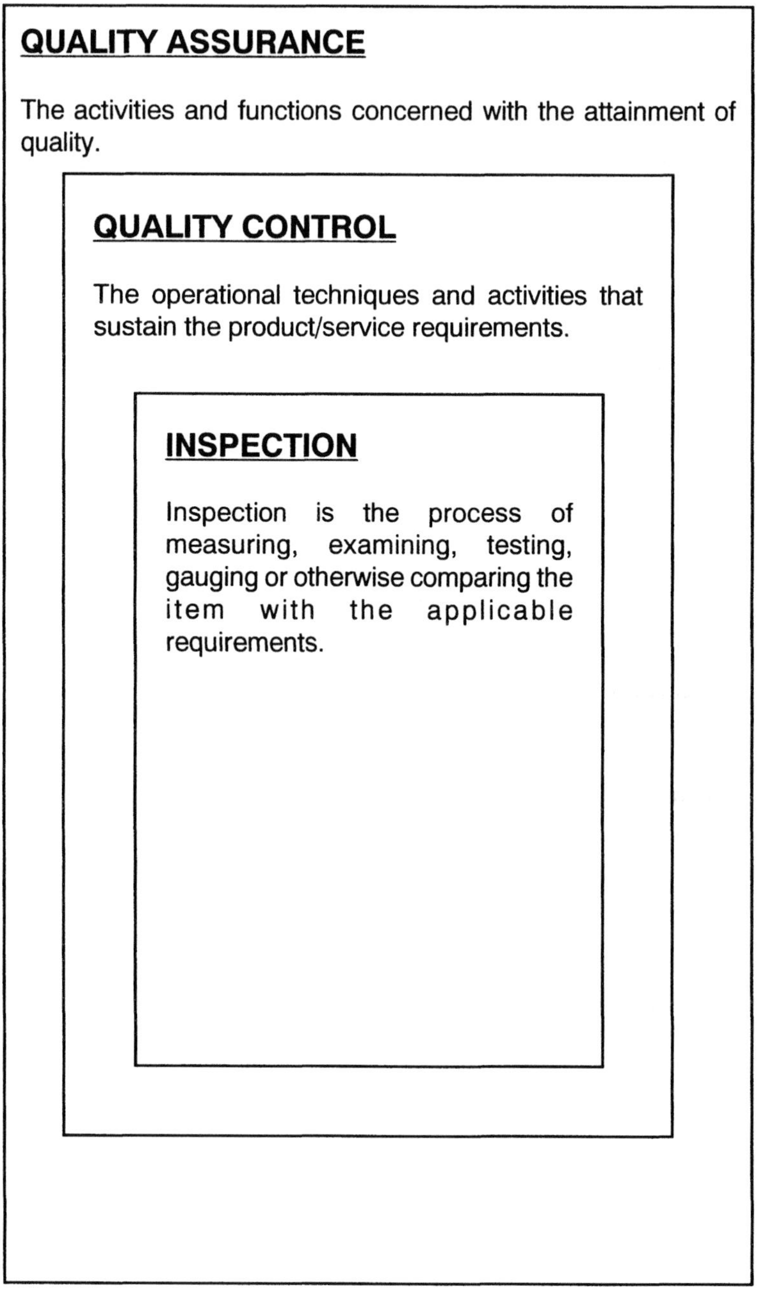

QUALITY ASSURANCE

The activities and functions concerned with the attainment of quality.

QUALITY CONTROL

The operational techniques and activities that sustain the product/service requirements.

INSPECTION

Inspection is the process of measuring, examining, testing, gauging or otherwise comparing the item with the applicable requirements.

Figure 10

Standards and Specifications

Introduction

Standards and specifications are playing an increasingly larger role in modern business. This is happening for many reasons, for example:

- Formal contracts are becoming more and more important, and a formal definition of the goods and services required is an integral part of this.
- Requirements are becoming more and more complex, and documented definitions are essential for proper understanding and agreement as to what the requirement actually is.
- Work teams are becoming larger and more complex too, so standards and specifications are essential to communication.

Definitions - General

Standard   -   model, a level of quality to which others must conform; the ideal!

Specification   -   to state definitely, to give details of, to indicate precisely; the description!

Code of Practice   -   details of what is practicable; the method!

Objective standards - also referred to as hard standards

- something tangible against which to compare your work
- existing independently of perception
- a material standard as opposed to a concept or idea
- undistorted by emotion or personal bias, e.g. gauge blocks; standard cell; noise level with decibel metre.

Subjective standards - also referred to as soft standards

- related to people's perception of what something might be
- something perceived
- standard based on a person's idea of what it ought to be e.g. noise level guessed at by a person; colour matching.

British Standards Definitions

Standard (from BS 0 Part 1 - 1981)

A standard is a technical specification or other document available to the public, drawn up with the co-operation and consensus or general approval of all interests affected by it, based on the consolidated results of science, technology and experience. It is aimed at the promotion of optimum community benefits and approved by a body recognised on the national, regional or international level.

Specification

The specification is the document that prescribes in detail the requirements with which the product or service has to comply.

"A specification is essentially a means of communicating the needs or intentions of one party to another".

The specification details the standard, although a specification need not have anything to do with a standard, i.e. it may be details of a 'one off'.

Codes of practice

Codes of practice should recommend good accepted practice as followed by competent practitioners (BS 0 Part 3).

NOTE: A code of practice is a recommendation only!

Product Specifications

A specification operates by naming explicitly and mentioning definitely the details of some projected work.

Key words in specification writing are *explicitly* and *definitely* and if it is to be any good, must be *unambiguous*. The specification is the document which describes and sets the standard of materials and workmanship. If it is ambiguous or loosely worded no one will know the standards they are expected to achieve.

The *aim* then of a specification is to state in words and phrases using drawings and diagrams, where relevant, the standard of work and quality required.

The specification is a means of communicating ideas from one person to another.

What is intended to happen? This is the question the *product designer* asks himself, hence from his ruminations a *design specification* is achieved. To make certain his wishes have been carried out an *acceptance test specification* is written and followed.

For new products there will be feedback to the designer from R&D (Research and Development), and other engineers enabling him to take corrective action, where necessary, to ensure everyone's objectives have satisfactorily been met, i.e. the quality element 'Fit for Purpose'.

For large orders, or an order of a specific nature, such as a missile system or a nuclear power plant, the *customer* may write his own specification. This will involve him indicating formally what he requires from a unit or system. The design specification will indicate how such requirements are to be achieved.

For day-to-day items, such as 'white goods', calculators and digital watches, the prospective customer does not get a chance to indicate his requirements, other than during a market research operation. On the other hand, today's customer has a wide range of competing goods from which to select. If one company will not give him what he wants another will.

A *customer's* specification may be all well and good, but only a full *design* feasibility study will identify the cost. It may be that the specification cannot be met, even with 'state of the art' technology, or that the cost would be prohibitive. The *reliability* specification may demand *zero defects* - or as near as *possible*. *Aero space* industry units are extremely expensive due to these criteria.

Standards and Specifications

A purely functional specification may not meet the customer's wishes, e.g, what happens if there is a power failure with a washing machine? Can the customer remove his laundry from the machine without a flood? The design specification must, therefore, see that a drainage point is fitted for this eventuality. In other words, specifications may include what must not happen as well as what must happen.

ISO 8402 lists twelve types of specification. It may be worth mentioning that one of these is a specification for disposal! If there is a policy to be *green* and *safe*, this will certainly refer to the disposal of, for example, refrigerators. An installation specification will ensure that no damage is done to the product during installation, which will affect its function. Installation specifications will also involve transport and packaging.

The designers and manufacturers of products are professional, whereas users may be non-technical or uneducated. This must be appreciated when writing user specifications.

Material Specifications

Introduction

To use materials for various purposes, the product designer and production engineer need detailed information to make the best choice from the viewpoint of a service and manufacturing requirement. The information is usually given as an engineering specification compiled by industry and organisations such as the British Standards Institution.

Types of specification:

The type of specification is important. For example, the designer is not really interested in the content of materials or their chemical make up but only in their performance during service.

Examples of specifications may include:

Design Specification: That might include a description of the primary purpose of an item, its style, function, performance, capacity, appearance, conditions of use, health and safety considerations, reliability, maintenance, materials, size, shape, colour, weight and tolerances allocated.

Service specification: This defines the services to be carried out, the level of performance required (including response times), roles and responsibilities, rules for escalating problems which cannot be resolved locally, and so on.

Test Specification: A document that describes in detail the objectives and method of conducting tests, including the data, the test environment, equipment, data, conditions, criteria for assessing results.

Customer Specification: What the customer requires from the product that may include a large amount from the design specification information above.

Whatever the definition of the particular type of specification, there will be much overlap between them.

Standards and Specifications

Body of the specification

Specifications may be written in a wide range of subjects and with a variety of objectives. The content of a specification depends upon the objectives to be achieved. They may include 'product reliability specifications', 'colour specification', 'weight specification', 'safety specification', etc.

The production engineer is interested in that part of the specification that affects how materials are formed during the manufacturing process. The production and quality engineers are both interested in that part of the specification that affects the manufacturing process, which in turn affects the service specification. To this end, the content of a material and its microstructures under various manufacturing conditions may be very relevant. Examples of this may include 'weld decay' problems with stainless steels, the various treatments encountered during the processing of aluminium alloys, the heat treatment effects of carbon steels, melting temperatures, castabilities and joinability etc.

Research and Development personnel together with test engineers and metallurgists, will be interested in all aspects including detailed metallurgical analysis.

Many properties may be specified in numerical terms, e.g. strength in Mn/m^2, others such as Malleability, may only be listed in order of the materials concerned.

Specification Writing

BS 7373 : 1991 Guide to the Preparation of Specifications provides rules for effective specification writing.

A few simple rules

Statements should be clear and concise not vague or ambiguous. In a specification for making tea, for example, it would be insufficient to state that the water must be clean. It would be necessary to specify the standard against which the quality of the water could be measured.

The purpose of a specification is to convey information. The ease with which this is achieved will be influenced by the style of presentation of this information. The standard provides guidance on this important aspect of specification preparation.

Introduction to Quality Assurance

A specification should always include a statement of its objectives. The objectives of a specification may be to give guidance, to list requirements, to educate, to inform or to instruct. Generally, one or more of these would be described in the introduction.

Clarity of text is essential. Double or hidden meanings should be eliminated. Technical terms should be referenced or defined. The final text should be suitable for inclusion in a legally binding contract.

Terminology

Specifications are written to be used by a variety of people. The technical level of the content may dictate the style to be adopted but, in the interests of clarity, the group, professional or non-professional, for whom the document is to be written, should be a major consideration.

The terminology used in the writing of a specification should be consistent with the specialist requirements of the subject and the comprehension of the user.

A specification written for use by members of a discrete profession would be expected to contain the terminology associated with the profession. A similar specification written for use by the consumer or user of a product service should avoid highly technical terminology and, where appropriate, should use a graphical approach.

Consistent terminology should be used throughout the specification and the use of the synonyms should be avoided. If a specification is part of a series, consistency with other specifications/standards should be ensured.

Terms or units used that could be misinterpreted or that are highly technical and pertinent to the subject matter of the specification should be defined.

Terms used in a special way for a particular specification should be defined.

Acronyms, no matter how well known to the author, should rarely be used and, if needed, should be preceded in the text by full terms the first time that they occur.

Standards and Specifications

In summary, since the aim is mutual understanding, clarity and simplicity are prime requirements, clarity of definition needs plain, simple language and the *specification* should be:

- As short as possible - unnecessary words or descriptions lead to lack of precision.

- Positive in meaning and intent.

- Unambiguous.

- Specific and precise.

- Free from vague generalities such as 'to be of good finish' or 'to be free from blemishes'. No questions such as 'how good?' or 'how free?' should remain unanswered.

- Numerical wherever possible, e.g. surface finish should be specified by the CLA (centre line average) value.

- Clear regarding the minimum acceptable level of quality or performance. Note: this may be affected by specifying the average and the range of characteristic required, such as a nominal dimension and the tolerance. For non-dimensional attributes, e.g. porosity, magnetic particle inspection indications of non-metallic inclusions, etc., the minimum acceptable level will be defined by the maximum size and number of blow-holes, and so on, in specified areas.

- Augmented by photographs, diagrams, models or samples where a precise numerical value cannot be given.

- Free from the common fallacy of calling for an unattainable 'desirable' target.

- Supported, whenever possible, by national or company standards but only after it has been confirmed that the standards themselves are clearly expressed and precise in their meaning.

- It is recommended that the convention for use of the words *'should'*, *'shall'*, *'must'* and *'will'* will be as follows:

- *'should'* for guidance clauses where there are no requirement or compliance inferred;
- *'shall'* or *'must'* when a requirement to comply with the contents of the clause is mandatory.

Suggested order of specification presentation

The suggested order of specification presentation is as follows:

•	Identification:	title, designation, number, authority;
•	Issue number:	publication history and state of issue, earlier related specifications;
•	Contents list:	structure of the specification;
•	Foreword:	the reason for writing the specification;
•	Introduction:	describes content in general and the technical aspects of objectives;
•	Scope:	statement of what the specification applies to;
•	Definitions:	terms used with meanings peculiar to the text;
•	Requirement/guidance/ methods/elements	the main body of specification;
•	Appendices:	examples, etc.;
•	Index:	cross references;
•	References:	to national, European, international standards or other internal company specifications.

Standards and Specifications

Product specifications as a basis for contract and auditing

Many large organisations such as Marks & Spencer rely totally on their suppliers delivering quality products and yet manage to maintain a very high reputation. This is achieved by requiring suppliers to comply strictly with product specifications. Typically, the specification for a shirt may be 50 to 100 pages long, detailing every element of manufacture. It would cover such things as cotton specification, including any starching or treatment to be applied to the textile, the gauge of the cotton, the length and positioning of stitching and so on. Marks & Spencer would then make regular surveillance visits to the supplier to audit that their specifications are being followed to the letter.

Specification amendments

From time to time, modifying the quality standard will be necessary. Thus, changes may be requested by the customer, or the designer may wish to improve or correct his design. Either way, it is usually the designer who will arrange for the drawings and specifications to be altered. Strict control will then be necessary to make sure that everyone concerned receives a revised copy, when they need it. The routine might be as follows:

- Copies of drawings and specifications are kept only in most suitably placed locations, usually drawing stores.

- When any drawing is issued or re-issued, the prescribed number of copies is sent to each. A person who requires a copy, borrows it from the nearest store, and his name is recorded.

- Where a re-issue is concerned, all copies of the previous issue are recalled and destroyed. Letting those in possession of the old issue destroy it is not satisfactory, because they will not always do so and then some time in the future, an obsolete issue will appear. Work will be made to it before the mistake is discovered.

- Showing clearly the alterations made to it and the date is usual for the modified drawing.

- Sometimes a modified drawing contains an indication of the urgency of the changes, e.g.

- *Type 1 modification* Very urgent. All partially completed work to the old drawings is to be scrapped and no more produced until the modified drawing can be used.

- *Type 2 modification* Partially completed work that is to the old drawing can be completed, but no more is to be made to it.

- *Type 3 modification* Changes to new issue as soon as convenient and economic. For example, when the tooling has to be renewed, or the present stocks of raw material run out.

The factory may wish to request a modification to the quality standard, to make the product easier and cheaper to produce. If the change is to be permanent, arrangements should be made with the designer to have the drawing altered and re-issued. Sometimes the request is more temporary. Perhaps the material specified cannot be obtained in time, or the factory wish to use up similar material already in stock. In such cases, the factory will request a *production permit*, authorising them to produce to the modified standard. Such permits are issued before production, and are only valid for a limited period. Permanent changes should be covered by a modification to the drawing.

Concession procedures

From time to time a batch may be produced outside drawing limits, which although the inspectors will rightly reject, nevertheless could be used. The factory will then ask for a *concession*. This allows them to use the product that has already been made, but they are not permitted to produce any more like it. The term *deviation* or *quality deviation* is sometimes used to embrace both production permits and concessions.

When any changes in the quality standard are authorised, care must be taken to deal with any repercussions, thus consequential changes may be necessary to certain components, otherwise the final performance and reliability of the product may be affected. Consequently, concessions are usually considered by a team of interested parties before it is agreed. It is important that long term preventive action is considered, e.g. re-design.

For the relationship between specifications measurement and process capability see the Section "Relationship between Specifications Measurement and Process Capability" on page 186.

Natural, Material and Subjective Standards

Introduction

The following is an extract from a letter written by the late C.R. Shotbolt - one time IQA Chief Examiner. The letter describes Mr C.R. Shotbolt's interpretation of the definition of various terms used in Measurements, Standards and Specifications.

Natural, material and subjective standards explained

Natural standards

Some units of measurements are referred to standards which are themselves natural phenomena. The metre is referred to the distance light travels in a vacuum in a specified time. Time is itself referred to a natural standard: the frequency of oscillation of the radiation emitted by isotope 133 of the atom of caesium. Temperature is also referred to a natural standard: the freezing point of water. These are all expressed here in a simplified form, the actual definition being much more complex. (Until recently the standard of length was the wavelength of the orange/red radiation in the spectrum of isotope 86 of the gas krypton. As length is still measured using interferometry involving the wavelength of light, either velocity or wavelength would be acceptable as an answer to this examiner's questions regarding the natural standard of length.) Any standards officer could set up a natural standard if he was prepared to buy the right equipment, and, for instance, calibrate reference gauges for length directly against the wavelength of light.

Material standards

The unit of mass, the kilogram, is referred to the International Kilogram which is a mass of an alloy of platinum and rhodium kept at the International Bureau of Standards at Sevres in France. It is a man-made object and has a mass of precisely one kg because international agreement was reached which said so. It cannot be precisely copied and if damaged or destroyed it cannot be exactly replaced.

If a trading standards officer wished to have his standard masses checked, they would have to be calibrated against reference masses held for the purpose at a suitable laboratory. These would have to be checked regularly against a copy of the British version of the international kg held at NPL. The British copy is checked regularly against the international kg in France. At each of these comparisons there might be an error as no measurement is exact, and, cumulatively, the greater the number of levels of comparison between the shop scales and the international kg the greater must be the allowance for error in the calibration of the scales. This is what is meant when reference is made to a hierarchy of measurements.

Subjective standards

There are cases when a decision as to whether or not an item should be accepted or rejected cannot depend upon an objective measurement but has to rely on a subjective judgement. Taste, smell, flaws in glass components or a paint finish are all examples. In many cases it is possible to have an example to which the inspector can refer and with which the item under test can be compared. Such an example is a subjective standard.

It has been suggested that, as the words 'natural standard', 'material standard' and 'subjective standard' do not appear in literature published by the British Standards Institution, they should not be used in an IQA syllabus. Although I had nothing to do with writing the syllabus, I cannot agree with this view. The words express exactly the differences between the different types of standards. Whereas BSI may be concerned with writing a specification on the measurement of length and another on the type of scales to be used for determining the mass of a particular item, I cannot see them having a need to distinguish between natural and material standards in order to explain the advantages of one over the other.

Incidentally, should we not get back to referring to British Standard Specifications rather than British Standards. It takes longer to say but it could avoid some confusion.

Measurements

Before the advent of the Industrial Revolution with all its ramifications, measurements were achieved by many varied and peculiar methods. Length by various parts of the anatomy; time, by using sun dials, hour glasses and burning candles; mass by using various lumps of metal.

Although there were many precursors to standardisation during the nineteenth century, many items were made in their entirety by one person with no need for interchangeability. Since the craftsman saw the whole job through from start to finish every part was made to fit all the other parts with little thought for standardisation. It was not until Henry Ford's re-engineering of the motor car that the concept became universal ("you can have any colour as long as it's black").

Today's industry, with its mass producing, interchangeable systems, need highly accurate length measurement. The pharmaceutical industry where mass needs to be measured in milligrams or less. The industry which has grown up around Einstein's theories, require timing devices accurate to a 10^{-12} seconds (pico's).

Natural, Material and Subjective Standards

Parameters and metrics

- A parameter is a variable which can be measured such as temperature, time, length, time to repair, shutter speed etc.
- A metric is the value of a parameter e.g. 150 mm, 5 seconds, 100° C.

Accuracy and precision

- Accuracy is how close a measurement is to the specified metric.
- Precision is the repeatability of such a measurement.

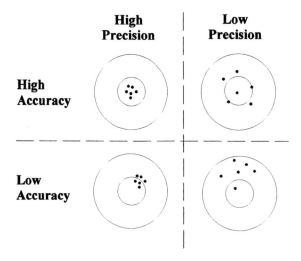

Figure 11

Introduction to Quality Assurance

Basic Standards of Measurements

Modern technology requires, where possible, absolute, unvarying, primary standards of measurement.

All measurements can be derived from the six fundamental units of the SI (Systems International) systems which are:

- mass
- length
- temperature
- electric current
- luminous intensity
- time

Mass (kilogram [kg])

The mass of a body is defined as the quantity of matter of which the body consists and can only be changed if matter is added to or subtracted from the body.

The fundamental unit of mass is the kilogram (kg) housed at the International Bureau of Weights and Measures at Sevres, France and takes the form of 90% platinum - 10% iridium alloy cylinder of equal height and diameter. Duplicates are held by various countries including Great Britain (in the custody of the National Physical Laboratory (NPL)) and may be compared with the prototype on request. Comparisons can be made with accurate scales to 1 in 10^8 precision.

NOTE: The prototype has not emerged from its box since 1941 and in practice transfer standards are compared with the average of seven duplicate standard masses.

Length (metre [m])

"The metre is the length of the path travelled by light in vacuum during a time interval of 1/299-, 792,458th of a second"

17th Conference Générale des Poids et Mesures, Paris, October 1983.

Historically, length standards were based upon material standards, i.e. the distance between two lines or the distance between two parallel ends of a bar.

Natural, Material and Subjective Standards

e.g.: Imperial Standard Yard:

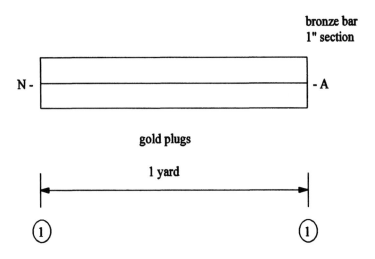

Figure 12

Such standards are prone to secular change (i.e. changes in dimension) over a period due to their metallurgical structure. Difficulty was experienced in transferring the accuracy to secondary and tertiary standards.

Temperature (Kelvin [K])

The Kelvin unit of thermodynamic temperature is the fraction 1/273.16 of the thermodynamic temperature of the triple point of water (273.16K)

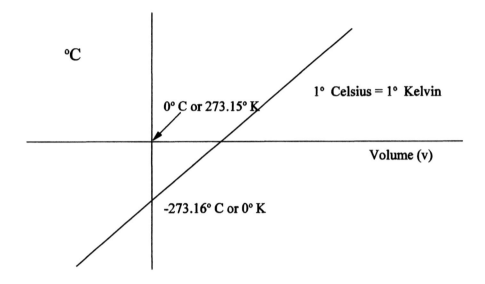

Figure 13

At low pressure, water may exist in its three forms, i.e. solid, liquid, gas at the same temperature. This is referred to as the triple point of water, which for intents and purposes is the temperature at which ice melts.

Practical Method of Calibrating Temperature Scales by Using Melting Gaseous Temperature of Various Substances.

e.g.:

liquid and gaseous oxygen -	182.97°C
ice and water -	0°C
water and vapour -	100°C
liquid sulphur and vapour -	444.6°C
solid silver and liquid silver -	960.5°C
solid gold and liquid gold -	1063°C

Secondary Scale (°C)

e.g. melting temperatures:

mercury	-	-38.8
lead	-	327
zinc	-	419.4
copper	-	1083
tungsten	-	3400

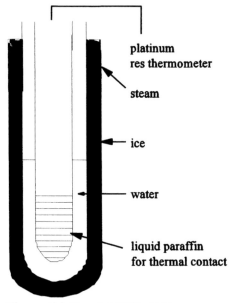

platinum
res thermometer

steam

ice

water

liquid paraffin
for thermal contact

Figure 14 Special NPL Cell

Electric current (Ampere [A])

The ampere is that constant current which, if maintained in two straight parallel conductors of infinite length of negligible circular cross-section placed 1m apart in a vacuum, would produce between those conductors a force equal to 2×10^{-7} Newtons per metre of length.

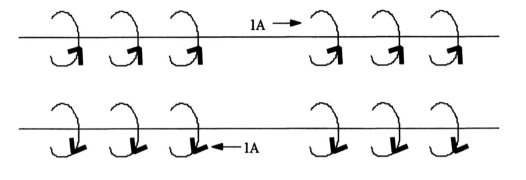

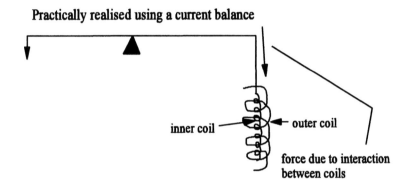

Practically realised using a current balance

inner coil — outer coil

force due to interaction between coils

Figure 15

Luminous Intensity (Candela [cd])

The candela is the luminous intensity in a given direction of a source that emits monochromatic radiation of frequency 540×10^{12} hertz and that has a radiant intensity in that direction of (1/683) watt per steradian(see below).

Practically a series of filament lamps are used to calibrate light sources.

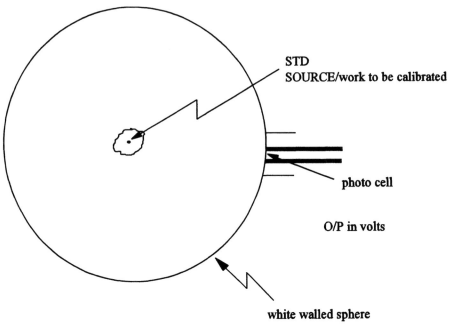

STD
SOURCE/work to be calibrated

photo cell

O/P in volts

white walled sphere

Figure 16

Time (second [s])

Fundamentally, all man-made clocks are set by some master clock in nature, e.g. swinging of a pendulum or the 24 hour rotation of the earth which used to be the standard of time - the complete rotation was timed by recording the instant a point on the earth passes under a chosen star in the sky on successive nights. The interval was divided into 24 x 60 x 60 = 86,400 parts which was defined as 1 second. However, there are errors due to the wobbles in the earth's rotation on its axis - the rate of rotation of the earth itself fluctuates unpredictably, hence, an error of 1 part in 20 million is apparent (not good enough for present day technology).

Atomic clocks - the second is now defined as the time for the cesium 133 atom to vibrate 9,192,631,770 times.

Cesium is a silvery metal liquid at room temperature. Other substances such as ammonia have been used to 'power' atomic clocks but cesium is the most accurate 1 part in 10^{13}. e.g. 1s in 300,000 years.

Supplemental Units

In addition to the six fundamental units of measurement, angles are defined as follows:

Plane angle (radian [rad])

The radian is the plane angle between two Radii of a circle which subtend an arc on the circumference equal in length to the radius.

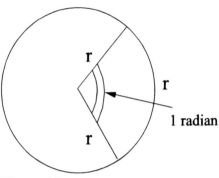

Figure 17

Solid angle (Steradian [Sr])
The steradian is the solid angle which, having its vertex in the centre of a sphere, prescribes an area of the surface of the sphere equal to that of a square with sides of length equal to the radius of the sphere

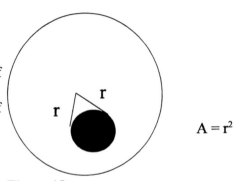

$$A = r^2$$

Figure 18

The plane angle and solid angle are examples of supplemental units

Base and Derived Units

The aforementioned standards all give rise to what are called *"base"* units. *"Derived"* units are as the name suggests derived from these base units.

For example, there are no less than three basic units to derive force. They are mass, length and time. The unit of force is the *Newton* and is derived as follows:

"One Newton is that unit of force which gives a mass of one kilogram an acceleration of one metre per second per second."

Calibration Concepts Techniques and Systems

Calibration is defined in ISO 8402/BS4778 and BS5233 as "All the operations for determining the values of the errors of measuring equipment (and, if necessary, to determine other metrological properties)".

The importance of regular calibration of gauges and measuring equipment, cannot be over-emphasised. An organisation's effectiveness and the quality and reliability of its products rely upon an efficient calibration system. Without such a system operating precision would be unknown.

Calibration is the checking of an instrument, article, or device against a known standard, usually of a much lower order than the primary standard.

Calibration is expensive, and the cost increases rapidly with reduced uncertainty, but the cost of being 'out of calibration' can be out of all proportion to the calibration cost. Roughly to halve the uncertainty increases costs tenfold. Health and safety aspects may also be factors to be considered.

Frequency of calibration

The frequency of calibration depends upon a number of factors:

- stability, sensitivity to change
- usage, frequency, handling
- environment,
- precision required.

Identification and status marking

Inspection, measuring and test equipment should be suitably identified together with its calibration status. This usually takes the form of a label with a serial number and a 'Calibration due' date so that the user can determine that it is safe to use.

Equipment not intended to determine the final quality of a product may not need to be calibrated. In such cases the equipment should be marked 'Uncalibrated'. Other suitable labelling may be appropriate in certain circumstances, for example, 'calibrate before use'.

Calibration Concepts Techniques and Systems

Uncertainty

Just as tolerances are applied to work for economic reasons, the same is used for gauges and instruments. The tolerance of a gauge is referred to as the uncertainty of measurement since there cannot be any confidence of anything less than that when using that particular gauge. When calibration procedures are prepared, they should define the uncertainty within which they are to be calibrated. In general, the gauge or instrument precision should be ten times better than the item it is used to measure. However, four or five times is often adequate. The fact remains that the precision to which we measure is limited by the next level of measurement.

Traceability

Calibration may be carried out in-house provided that the standard used for calibration is itself calibrated to traceable standards. All technological quantities have standards which are traceable to reliable primary standards.

Assuming that each subsequent checking media is ten times as accurate as the previous one the following table shows the traceable steps of calibration from the work to national primary standards.

CALIBRATION DEVICE	UNCERTAINTY mm	TYPE OF STD	ORGANISATION
WORK	0.01	---------------	
measured by	↓	↓	
MICROMETER	0.001	Workshop	Workshop
calibrated by	↓	↓	↓
SLIP GAUGE	0.0001	Tertiary	Inspection room
calibrated by	↓	↓	↓
OPTICAL FLAT	0.00001	Secondary	Standards laboratory
Calibrated by	↓	↓	↓
LIGHT	0.000001	Primary	NAMAS[1] accredited laboratory

---

[1]   In a later section the role of the National Assessment and Measurement Accreditation Scheme (NAMAS) is explained in more depth.

Introduction to Quality Assurance

There may, of course, be other checks within the calibration procedures of any feature which may impair the use of the equipment, e.g. flatness and parallelism of micrometer anvils.

The above chart will obviously vary from industry to industry, and from physical quantity to physical quantity, but the principle remains the same. It is obviously impossible to go from a workshop situation, directly to the primary standard. The direct traceable link from the lowest possible situation, e.g. length in a workshop, mass in the grocer's shop, ordinary everyday time keeping, to the primary standard, in each case, must practically be via a well-organised system.

Calibration Systems

The following list describes the key requirements of a calibration system as required in ISO 9001.

a.   Identify all measuring equipment with a unique identification, e.g. serial number and its calibration status. See Table - Calibration Labelling.

Table 1 Calibration Labelling

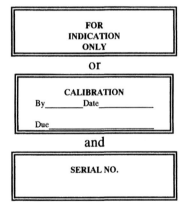

b.   Establish the frequency with which the measuring equipment needs to be checked, e.g. for a set of weighing scales this could be every six months.

c.   Define procedures that describe the calibration system (measuring equipment recall procedure etc.). This can be a card file; one card for each piece of measuring equipment. The cards are then filed in next-calibration-date order, so at the beginning of each month the equipment that requires calibration is identified and located.

Table 2 A typical Calibration History Sheet

CALIBRATION HISTORY RECORD SHEET					
Equipment Type:			Model No.:		
Serial No.:			Size:		
Calibration Frequency:			Procedure No.:		
DATE OF LAST CALIBRATION	DATE OF NEXT CALIBRATION	DATE OUT/IN	LOCATION	RESULT OF CALIBRATION	REMARKS

d. Detail the individual calibration procedures for each type of measuring equipment. For weighing scales this could be having some calibrated weights placed on the scales and checking the readings correspond with the calibrated weights.

e. Ensure that the inspection and test equipment has the necessary accuracy and precision. For the weighing scales example the accuracy of the calibrated weights could be 10% of the accuracy of the scales.

f. Define the procedures that describe the activities necessary if the results of calibration highlight equipment error. If the weighing scales were found to be in error when calibrated and used for weighing drugs, then it may be necessary to take corrective action, possibly to recall the drugs.

g. Establish calibration history records showing the previous calibration results. **Table 2** shows a typical calibration history sheet.

h. Determine the necessary environmental conditions suitable for accurate calibration.

i. Detail appropriate handling, preservation and storage procedures.

j. Ensure that equipment is sealed to avoid any possibility of adjustments that could invalidate the calibration setting. For the weighing scales - any adjustment screws would need to be sealed.

Introduction to Quality Assurance

Calibration and automatic test equipment (ATE)

ATE equipment is computer controlled test equipment. Frequently used for the testing of assemblies and sub-assemblies. Typically these types of machines have either an 'in circuit' or a 'functional' test capability (or a combination of both).

'In circuit' testing confirms that a circuit board has been manufactured correctly (i.e. finds short circuits, open circuits and components that are outside tolerance limits). The in circuit tester usually interfaces with the unit under test (UUT) via a 'bed of nails' fixture that has one pin for every electrical node. This allows measuring of characteristics between any electrical connections (e.g. across each component).

Figure 19 shows a typical ATE set up. 'Functional' testing interfaces to the UUT either via a few pins in a bed of nails fixture (e.g. maybe one pin per 100 connections) or by way of flying leads. This means of testing could be used for a printed circuit board or a whole assembly. A 'good' functional test will find any manufacturing defects plus any parameters that are not within design specifications.

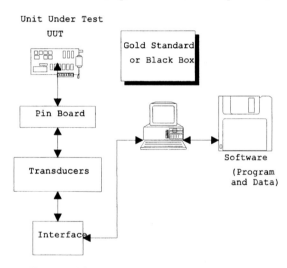

Figure 19 Typical Automatic Test Equipment

Functional testing is quick to highlight a failure whereas in circuit testing is quicker to pinpoint where the failure lies, (i.e. identifies the fault location down to component level). A typical use for ATE is in medium to high volume production or for high level technology, such as the space industry.

The use of automatic testing ensures that all the assemblies are tested to within pre-defined tolerances. The testing becomes objective as opposed to subjective. The QA personnel would need to ensure that the pre-selected tolerances are correct. Once proven this method of testing provides a very high degree of repeatability plus the availability of automatically logged test results for use in Statistical Quality Control (SQC) and real time fault analysis (RTFA).

61

Calibration Concepts Techniques and Systems

Calibration of the equipment, i.e. transducers and connection between the equipment under test and the computer; the transducer and connection between the computer and the pin board can be tested, although not completely, by the use of a 'Gold Standard' or 'Black Box' This 'Gold Standard' could be a specially selected unit that is a known standard or quality. This 'Gold Standard' would be regularly re-tested by the ATE to confirm that the hardware is working satisfactorily.

Validation and verification of the test software program and data for ATE could consist of:

a.   the program to drive the ATE,
b.   the sequencer which runs the sequence and determines which test to perform,
c.   and the test data (both target value and tolerance), the program and sequencer will need to be validated and verified. The test data will need to be checked.

Standardising Organisations

Introduction

In this section, an overview of some of the relevant certification schemes, standards and guides, and quality-related bodies is presented. It is not intended to be exhaustive but merely to introduce the more common ones.

Company and Industry Standards

In addition to the public standards described below, most manufacturing industries also have extensive internal standards. For example, there are British Standards for a huge range of goods, agreed over the years by the relevant industry bodies. The European Union has also set hundreds of mandatory product standards for goods affecting health, safety and the environment, as described in a later section.

Most individual manufacturers will also have comprehensive production plans for each product they manufacture. These plans are at least the equivalent of internal standards, and typically cover every aspect of the production process.

These plans might include any or all of the following:

- product design
- key product and process quality criteria
- machine and production line set-up
- controls and settings
- raw materials requirements and standards
- processing instructions and methods
- in-process and final monitoring and testing methods and criteria
- product identification and traceability requirements and methods
- packaging
- storage, handling and delivery handling requirements.

Company standards are normally maintained by a central group (e.g. the quality department or drawing office) and are based on a combination of public standards and the technology and management methods that the company will actually use to make the products. Control and enforcement of internal standards is just as important as control and enforcement of public standards, and for the same reasons. No one in the whole organisation has enough knowledge or experience of all the factors affecting the product to be able to change the standard at will, and variations should only be allowed with full consultation and approval and only under properly controlled conditions.

Company and industry standards are much less the norm in service companies, partly because services are perceived as much more a matter of personal skill and experience, partly because the quality of the service is judged by more subjective criteria, and partly because the culture of objective standards has yet to mature in this environment. The same is largely true of IT, R&D organisations and government departments.

Approval and Certification Schemes

An approval or certification scheme implies that someone is approving someone else against an agreed standard. There are basically two types of standard. One applies to management systems as a whole, the other applies more specifically to products or processes. One of the first major approving body in the UK was the British Standards Institute although there are now many others that specialise in specific areas.

Certification invariably means that the firm seeking certification must establish documented systems of Quality Control which satisfy the requirements of the relevant standard. This usually requires first, that the systems and processes must be documented and second, that the systems and activities in operation comply with the documents. This is verified by appropriate external and internal audits. Once a firm is approved, periodic audits are carried out to verify that the firm is continuing to comply.

Certification Schemes for Quality Systems

Quality assurance management system (QAMS) - The management of quality

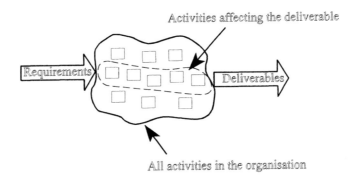

Activities affecting the deliverable

Requirements

Deliverables

All activities in the organisation

Figure 20

The scope of the application of a Quality Assurance Management System (QAMS) must be clearly defined.

Typically, activities excluded from a QAMS are occupational health and safety at work, environmental issues, personnel functions other than training, internal finance and accounting and marketing.

Quality System Standards apply only to the quality processes. They do not specify product or service grades. These are set either by other standards or codes of practice pertinent to the industry or, by the customer, or by the supplier. For example:

- Legislation e.g. safety regulations
- British Standards (or equivalent) for products and Codes of Practice
- Customer specifications
- Supplier specifications

Note: Where there is continuous customer interface during delivery, i.e. services, there are two parallel processes to consider:
   a) what is being delivered and
   b) the delivery process itself.

This often includes soft standards (attitudes and manner), which are subjective, and hard standards, which are directly verifiable. For example:

Soft Standards	-	attitudes of server; appearance; helpfulness; empathy; advice/counsel etc.
Hard Standards	-	accuracy; response time; etc.

ISO 9000[2]

This standard specifies the requirements for a general Quality Assurance System. It is not intended to be a company specific quality standard but a practical standard for quality systems which can be applied to any industry.

The principles of ISO 9000 are applicable regardless of the size of the firm. It identifies the basic disciplines and specifies the shape of a management quality assurance system to ensure that the supplier meets the customer requirements.

ISO 9000 is an internationally recognised standard and is simply 'common sense' set down on paper in an organised way. The standard comprises 20 requirements which firms must address to gain certification. Depending on the scope of operation of the firm, some of the requirements may not be applicable. While the standard specifies what activities need to be addressed it does not say how. Most successful firms are already applying the underlying principles embodied in ISO 9000. However, often the quality assurance systems may not be fully documented and there may not be records which confirm observance of the specified quality assurance system.

Suppliers can use ISO 9000 as a guide when setting up their own systems.

Customers can specify ISO 9000 in the contract as a means of controlling the quality of goods and services they are purchasing. ISO 9000 may augment the customer's own product specific standards.

Third parties can use ISO 9000 as a basis for assessing a supplier's management system and, consequently, its ability to produce satisfactory goods and services. Firms successful in gaining a certificate are listed in the Department of Trade and Industry (DTI) Register of Firms of Assessed Capability.

---

[2]   Note; ISO 9000 is used here in the generic sense to refer to ISO 9001, ISO 9002 and ISO 9003. See "The ISO 9000 family of Standards"

It should be noted that ISO 9000 does not specify the quality of the product or service directly but the quality of the system which produces them. The quality of the product or service is prescribed by the purchaser and agreed by the supplier in a contract of products or services or requirements are prescribed by the supplier which are perceived as satisfying a market need.

The cost of achieving and maintaining certification status remains entirely with the firm seeking certification.

Certification

To register to the world that a company has installed and operates a QAMS in accordance with ISO 9000, there are a number of third party (independent) Accreditation bodies that can certify to that effect. If certification by BSI (or other accredited body) is intended, they will first carry out an assessment of the organisation comprising an adequacy audit on the Quality Manual followed by an initial compliance audit on site. Companies who qualify are registered in the DTI Register of Companies of Assessed Capability. After registration, surveillance audits will be carried out usually twice a year for as long as registration is maintained. Needless to say that all this is at the supplier's expense.

What the standard is about

ISO 9000 is about managing and controlling quality rather than leaving things to chance. What this means is:

a. Commitment at the highest level that the organisation is serious about installing and maintaining a Quality Assurance Management System. This results in a Quality Policy Statement.

b. Analysing and agreeing the best way to ensure that all quality determinants are identified and controlled.

Where existing methods of working are known to be effective and efficient, the aim should be to describe them as they are rather than trying to change everyone to work to new unknown methods.

c. Allocating responsibilities for quality. Since quality is everyone's business, what this means in practice must be spelled out in writing. Otherwise, quality ends up being nobody's business.

In particular, a management representative must be identified with the specific responsibility of maintaining the QAMS and resolving issue of conflict in relation to the attainment of quality.

d. Documenting the arrangements for controlling quality. In addition to the Quality Manual and Procedures Manual, all other documentation relating to quality must be available and controlled to ensure its current status is at the correct issue.

Since every organisation, and possibly every department in that organisation, will have its own customs and practice, the standard allows for each organisation to decide how it intends to address the requirements of the standard. Therefore, quality manuals and the supporting documented system will be unique to the organisation concerned.

Much of the required documentation will already exist within the organisation but because there is so much documentation it needs to be organised into a manageable form.

e. Being able to demonstrate, usually through relevant records, that the system is being adhered to.

f. Carrying out regular internal audits to identify and correct deviations from agreed procedures.

Introduction to Quality Assurance

The ISO 9000 family of standards

Generally, ISO 9000 refers to a family of standards and guides related to the management of quality. There is ISO 9000, ISO 9001, ISO 9003 and ISO 9004.

Specifically, **ISO 9000** comprises four parts as follows:

ISO 9000-1:1994   Quality management and quality assurance standards - Part 1: Guide to selection and use.

ISO 9000-2:1993   Quality management and quality assurance standards - Part 2: Generic guidelines for the application of ISO 9001, ISO 9002 and ISO 9003.

ISO 9000-3:1991   Quality management and quality assurance standards - Part 3: Guidelines for the application of ISO 9001 to the development, supply and maintenance of software.

ISO 9000-4:1994   Quality management and quality assurance standards - Part 4: Guide to dependability programme management.

Notice that these are all guides. However, ISO 9000-3 in particular is often used as though it were a standard.

ISO 9001, ISO 9002 and ISO 9003 are the conformance standards. They specify what must be done if an organisation wishes to obtain a certificate. These are the standards the certification body will use to assess an organisation's quality system. Only one of these standards will apply to an organisation depending on its scope of activities as follows:

ISO 9001:1994   Quality Systems - Model for quality assurance in **design, development, production, installation and servicing.** (Formerly BS 5750 Part 1)

ISO 9002:1994   Quality Systems - Model for quality assurance in **production, installation and servicing.** (Formerly BS 5750 Part 2)

     A subset of ISO 9001. It is intended for organisations having no design and service functions. ISO 9002 applies to the majority of organisations.

ISO 9003:1994

Quality Systems - Model for quality assurance in **final inspection and test.** (Formerly BS 5750 Part 3)

A subset of ISO 9002 for organisations where the quality of the product can be confidently verified by final inspection. These are a very small minority. Some certification bodies do not even acknowledge it, arguing that all organisations have a process.

ISO 9004

This is a set of guides intended to provide further clarification of the various aspects of the three compliance standards.

ISO 9004-1:1994

Quality management and quality system elements - Part 1: Guidelines (Replaces BS 5750 Part 0 Section 0.2)

ISO 9004-2:1991

Quality management and quality systems elements - Part 2: Guidelines for services.

ISO 9004-3:1993

Quality management and quality systems elements - Part 3: Guidelines for processed materials.

ISO 9004-4:1993

Quality management and quality systems elements - Part 4: Guidelines for quality improvement.

It was originally intended that this list of guides should be extended as part of ISO 9004. However, some of them have now been published outside of the ISO 9000 family as follows:

ISO 10005: 1995

Quality Management Guidelines for quality plans (originally ISO 9004-5/BS 5750 Part 11)

ISO 10007: 1995

Quality Management Guidelines for configuration management
(Originally ISO 9004-6/BS 5750 Part 12)

ISO 10013: 1995

Guidelines for developing quality manuals

Defence Standards (Def Stan's) and AQAP's

This was the forerunner of the British Standard and subsequently the ISO standard. However, it was essentially a second party approval scheme applicable to the Ministry of Defence and NATO contracts. Apart from some exceptional overseas contracts the Allied Quality Assurance Publications (AQAP) have now been superseded with Def Stans 91, 92 and 93 which invoke the respective ISO standard.

As with ISO 9000 registered firms, there is a similar register of AQAP firms of assessed capability which is used as a basis for selecting MOD or NATO contractors. The appropriate level of ISO 9000 standard would be called up in the contract.

Where the customer carries out the assessment of the supplier, this is known as a second party assessment. Unlike third party assessments, such as those carried out by BSI, the costs of initial and subsequent re-assessments are borne by the purchaser, i.e. MOD or NATO. In addition, primary contracts are allocated a Quality Assurance Representative (QAR) who monitors that the terms of the contract are adhered to, including compliance with the relevant quality system standard.

Product Standards

BSI Kitemark

The British Standard Kitemark is a registered trade mark owned by BSI and may only be used by manufacturers licensed by BSI under a particular Kitemark scheme. The appearance of this distinctive symbol on a product indicates that BSI has independently tested samples of the product against the appropriate British Standard and confirmed that the standard has been complied with in every respect. The manufacturer will also be required to produce and maintain a Quality System based on ISO 9000 'Quality Systems'. This Quality System will be assessed as part of the certification process and should set out the organisation, responsibilities, procedures and methods involved in manufacturing the product.

BSI safety mark

This mark appears on a number of products which conform to British Standards specifically concerned with safety or to the safety requirements of standards which cover other product characteristics as well. As with the Kitemark, the Safety Mark can only be used by manufacturers licensed under a Safety Mark scheme which involves an assessment procedure similar to that of the Kitemark.

Other inspectorates/certification bodies

There are now over sixty accredited organisations who grant certification to the companies who conform to ISO 9000. In addition, there are a number of industry specific standards set by certain industries. These include:

CAA	-	Civil Aviation Authority
PVQAB	-	Pressure Vessels Quality Assurance Board
CEGB	-	BS5882 QA Nuclear
DHSS	-	Good Manufacturing Practices/Good Laboratory Practices applicable in the medical industry and other situations where hygiene is of special importance.

Accreditation of Certification Bodies

Apart from approval schemes there are a number of national bodies which offer services in the field of quality. The standards of these services are in turn controlled and maintained to nationally agreed criteria.

The United Kingdom Accreditation Service operates accreditation schemes for Certification Bodies. These are National Accreditation of Certification Bodies (NACB) for the accreditation of Certification Bodies and the National Assessment and Measurement Accreditation Service (NAMAS) for accreditation of Calibration Laboratories or Test Houses. NACB use EN 45000 series to accredit Certification Bodies who certify organisations using the BS EN ISO9000 series of standards. NAMAS use the EN45001 (M10) as the basis for their accreditation.

Diagrammatically the hierarchy of these bodies would be as shown in the diagram **Figure 21**.

The National Accreditation of Certification Bodies (NACB)

The NACB operates a system of accreditation of Certification Bodies such as BSI, Lloyds, Bureau Veritas Quality International, United Register of Systems etc., who certify organisations using the BS EN ISO9000 series.

The purpose of NACB is to assess the independence and technical competence of UK certification bodies to the requirements of EN45011/2/3.

EN45011 is the standard for certification bodies when issuing certificates of product conformity.

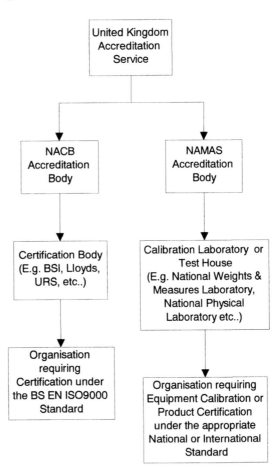

Figure 21 Accreditation Bodies

Accreditation Of Certification Bodies

EN45012 is the standard for the certification bodies own Quality Management System usually based on ISO9001, i.e. the Certification Bodies Quality Manual, Quality Manager, Internal Audit procedure etc.

EN45013 is used to assess the competence of the certification bodies own personnel (assessors).

Together, these standards cover the structure, operation and management of the certification body.

Once the certification body is accredited, it is granted the right to use the Tick and Crown symbol. This symbol denotes that the certification body has been accredited in a particular industrial sector. Not all certification bodies are accredited in all industrial sectors. For example, some certification bodies are not accredited by the NACB in the medical or software sectors. In this situation, certification bodies may still assess and issue certificates to companies working in the medical and software industrial sectors. However, the certificates issued cannot carry the Tick and Crown.

Figure 22

The accreditation process is very similar to the ISO9000 certification process with application, pre-assessment, adequacy audit, full assessment and, if successful, accreditation.

Once a certification body is accredited by the NACB, then any organisations certificated by that body can appear in the DTI QA register of approved companies, together with the certification bodies own guide e.g. BSI Buyers Guide.

The national assessment and measurement accreditation service (NAMAS)

The purpose of NAMAS, the National Assessment and Measurement Accreditation Service is to assess, accredit and monitor test houses and calibration laboratories. The value of this accreditation is based on the need to ensure that products are produced to specification and that products are safe. Note: product certification not management system certification. NAMAS accredited laboratories can provide this necessary assurance of the competence of calibration and testing houses. It is this competence which will avoid the need for multiple assessment of calibration and testing laboratories. NAMAS certificates of calibration and test reports have now been recognised by organisations such as British Telecom, Ministry of Defence, Rolls Royce etc. NAMAS are also involved with gaining agreement on the recognition of other National Schemes and, as a consequence, International acceptance of the competence of the accredited laboratory.

Following the stringent examination to the requirements usually of the standards M10 and M11[3], laboratories would then be authorised to use the formal certification and reports to record the results of any measurements and tests taken. These standards are very similar to ISO9001 but with reference to calibration.

The method of certification is also very similar to the approach that would be adopted by the NACB or any other accreditation body. There is an application. The laboratory documentation is examined. There is a pre-assessment and then a full assessment of the laboratory.

Any non-compliance to M10 and M11 would then be reported. If any were found, corrective action would be taken and on satisfactory completion of these corrective actions NAMAS would offer the laboratory accreditation. The NAMAS certificate would then be issued and the surveillance visits would then commence on a regular basis. Once certificated the accredited laboratory services would be publicised through the NAMAS directory of accredited laboratories.

These accredited laboratories can include commercial calibration laboratories and test houses as well as laboratories forming part of larger organisations such as a manufacturing company, university, or some government organisation.

Only laboratories accredited by NAMAS may use the NAMAS logo in conjunction with their accreditation number. This is an important distinction and one which is carefully guarded by NAMAS to the extent that forging of these NAMAS certificates has resulted in custodial sentences for the misuse of these certificates.

A typical example of one of these NAMAS certificated reports is shown in **Figure 23**

---

[3]   M10 & M11 are similar to BS7500 series, EN45001 & EN45002 and ISO Guides 25 & 54. These documents cover the accreditation standard and regulations for measurement and calibration facilities.

Accreditation Of Certification Bodies

Figure 23 Typical Calibration Certificate

CERTIFICATE OF CALIBRATION

Issued by the Quality Management & Training Laboratory

Date of Issue: 13 July 1995　　　　**Serial No: 1234**

NAMAS

Quality Management & Training Laboratory
P O Box No 172
Guildford Surrey GU2 6FJ

Tel: 01483 453511
Page 1 of 1 pages

CALIBRATION NO:
Approved Signatories
Mr F Tickle BA CEng MIMechE
MIEE MIQA
Signed *F Tickle*
Mr G Vorley MSc MIQA
Signed *G Vorley*

CUSTOMER:　　　　　　Vakes Ltd Benley Park Guildford
DESCRIPTION:　　　　　1 off Micrometer to measure 0 to 25mm ± 0.01mm
SERIAL NO:　　　　　　12345
DATE OF CALIBRATION:　13 July 1995

REPORT

BASIS OF TEST:　　　　A specified tolerance of ±1%
DIMENSIONAL:　　　　　The gauge was measured for pressure at seven positions across the
　　　　　　　　　　　range of the equipment using the Butenburgh testing rig. Serial No
　　　　　　　　　　　123456.

The results were taken at 20°c +/- 2°c

MEASURING POSITIONS		RESULTS (mm)
1	0 mm	0
2	5	5.001
3	10	9.995
4	15	15.008
5	20	19.996

Uncertainty of measurement ± .5%
All measurement values were within the tolerance specified above

Signature *F Tickle*

The uncertainties are for a confidence probability of not less than 95%.

CE Marking

Introduction

The European Union (EU) has a series of Directives on General Safety and Product Liability. These Directives were agreed by all Member States and will affect all businesses that design, manufacture or export into the European Union. The purpose of these directives is to:

$C\epsilon$

o Create a legal requirement for all the Member States to adopt these agreed, common and harmonised technical standards.

Figure 25 The CE Mark

o Prohibit the supply of goods which do not conform to these technical standards. The CE mark is shown in the diagram **Figure 25** and is used to declare that a product complies with all relevant standards.

o Promote free trade within the EU by removing local or national technical standards that may have been a barrier to free trade. The CE mark is the guarantee that the product will not be challenged at national boundaries.

Listed in the table below are the Directives adopted since the resolution of May 1985.

Table 3 EU Directives

Title	Directive
Acoustics	90/270/EEC
Active Implantable Medical Devices	90/385/EEC
Appliances Burning Gaseous Fuels	90/396/EEC
Cable-Way Installations	94/C70/07
CE Labels	91/C160/07
Construction Products	89/106/EEC
Electrical Equipment designed for use within certain voltage limits	73/23/EEC
Electromagnetic Compatibility	89/336/EEC

Title	Directive
Machinery	89/392/EEC
Medical Devices	93/42/EEC
New Hot-Water Boilers fired with Liquid or Gaseous Fuels	92/42/EEC
Non-automatic Weight Instruments	89/384/EEC
Personal Protective Equipment	89/686/EEC
Pressure Equipment	93/C246/10
Recreational Craft	92/C123/07
Safety of Toys	88/378/EEC
Satellite Earth Stations	3/97/EEC
Simple Pressure Vessels	87/404/EEC
Telecommunications Terminal Equipment	91/263/EEC
VDU Ergonomics	90/270/EEC 91/2303

It is a criminal act to supply goods which do not conform to the harmonised standard and consequently the penalties are quite severe. They include the supplier being required to remove all similar products from the EU. The persons found guilty will have a criminal record and can be imprisoned for up to three months and fined £5,000 per offence.

Outlined below are some typical steps necessary to ensure designs and products meet the CE marking requirements and any other appropriate national or international regulations and directives. There are some reference documents which include:

> Outline Technical Construction File Contents
> Outline Declaration of Conformance
> Outline Declaration of Incorporation

The procedure below embraces the sequence of events necessary to ensure compliance with Directives or Regulations. (This needs to include both new or modified product or production equipment and other modified purposes such as production.) The procedure also needs to include the steps necessary when incorporating other suppliers equipment into a company's own products.

Introduction to Quality Assurance

There may be a need to review existing Purchasing and Goods Inwards Inspection Procedures to ensure that they adequately cover the CE marking requirements and do not need enhancement.

CE Marking Procedure Guidelines

The table - CE Marking Overview, indicates the general shape to addressing the CE mark requirements. CE marking is self-certification and does not usually involve third party registration. In other words the supplier is claiming compliance with a particular requirement as supported by their own checks, tests, approvals etc.

The left-hand side is a list of all of the supplier's products. At the top is a list of any applicable requirements, regulations or directive. The output from this analysis will be the central matrix showing where a Product or Design needs to show compliance with a requirement, then certain documentation will need to be produced. Namely the creation

Table 4 CE Marking Overview

Directives / Products	Acoustics	Electrical Equipment	Electromagnetic Compatibility	Machinery	Pressure Vessels	Other CE Directives
Product A	✓		✓			
Product B		✓				
Product C	✓					
Product D				✓		
Product E						
Product n						

The tick ✓ indicates that there is a Statutory Requirement or Directive that the particular product needs to comply with.

of a design Technical Construction File which provides evidence of compliance with the necessary requirements. Together with the Declaration of Conformance and/or Incorporation (in the case of the suppliers products being incorporated in another product), i.e. documentation that goes with the product to show compliance.

Input to the CE marking process: A current, new product[4] or significant design change to a new product must be reviewed to ensure that it complies with all current directives and regulations. Any modification to production or other types of equipment will also need to be reviewed to ensure compliance with all directives and regulations. Reviews will need to include any new directives or where the directives have become mandatory[5], i.e. the transition period has ended.

---

[4]   A product referred to here is a generic product not an individual variation, i.e. the individual product variation does not impact on the essential requirements of a directive or is not covered in an existing Technical Construction File.

[5]   The technical expression is *Transition Ends* - the period between in force and mandatory.

Introduction to Quality Assurance

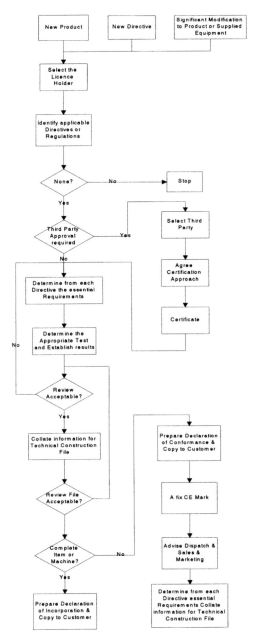

Figure 26 CE Marking Sequence

CE Marking

CE marking sequence: See **Figure 26**. Firstly it is necessary to identify a Product Licence Holder[6]. Once the person has been established, then a review can take place.

REVIEW 1: Identify any directives or regulations which are applicable, e.g. Electrical Equipment, Simple Pressure Vessels, Electromagnetic Compatibility and Machinery. Taking due account of any directives which are in force and transition has ended. See **Table 3** for guidance.

If Third Party Certification[7] is required (only as a result of the directive) e.g. Pressure Vessels, then the certification body will need to be selected. Next the test standard and certification approach[8] will need to be agreed with the certification body.

Having established the appropriate directives then each of the requirements needs to have been addressed. One way of ensuring complete coverage of the directives' requirements is by copying[9] the Directive, then adding and completing three columns, headed; Requirements, Test and Results. The following table shows the Directives Requirements (in normal print) and adjacent to each requirement (in script) the tests carried out to confirm compliance, together with the test results.

---

[6]   The person responsible for compliance

[7]   A Notified Body such as BSI can provide an E.C. type examination certificate

[8]   Samples Tested by an Independent Testing Body, Audit by an Independent Body, Testing by the suppliers etc.

[9]   Copying is acceptable

Introduction to Quality Assurance

Table 5 Typical example of part of a completed Directive Review

Requirement	Test	Result
The suppliers Designed Items		
1.1.4 Light Suitable	*Visual*	*OK*
1.2.1 Safety & Reliability of the Controls	*Visual* *Enclosure Test*	*OK* *OK*
Subcontract Sourced Items		
1.5.1 Electrical Supply	*Add Declaration of Incorporation required from Suppliers to Purchase Order*	*Added Declaration of Incorporation Provided*

REVIEW 2: The above information is then examined by the Licence Holder and possibly the Department Head and if appropriate the Buyer. If acceptable the last page could be signed by the Licence Holder.

The information detailed in the Table of Contents for the Technical Construction File can then be compiled. See Appendix Technical Construction File Contents List.

REVIEW 3: All of the information in the Technical Construction File can then be examined and reviewed by the Licence Holder and the Departmental Manager. If these are the same person then by a peer. If acceptable then archive the information for a minimum of ten years after cessation of manufacture. If the product is a complete machine then a Declaration of Conformity needs to be completed and a copy sent to the customer. A CE mark can then be added to the machine (usually adjacent to the rating plate). Sales & Marketing can be advised that the sales literature can be updated to indicate that the product conforms to specified directives. The dispatch documentation will usually need to carry the same information.

If the product is not a complete item (e.g. a sub-assembly) then a Declaration of Incorporation can be produced and a copy sent to the customer.

CE Marking

Note: Every piece of equipment that is to be sold for use in the European Community must be affixed with a CE mark. This mark must be affixed to one or more of the following:

i. The equipment
ii. The equipment packaging
iii. The equipment instructions for use
iv. The equipment guarantee certificate.

Typical Technical Construction File Contents List:

i. Contents List
ii. Copy of Directive which includes the tests and results essential to show compliant with the directive
iii. Drawing List (including issue status) and Drawings
iv. Calculation List and Calculations
v. Manuals (User, Operation, Maintenance, Installation, Commissioning etc.)
vi. Any Quality Plans or ISO9000 records
vii. Copy of the Declaration of Conformance or Certificate of Adequacy of equipment supplied
viii. Bibliography of the Standard Used

Cost of Quality

Introduction

The Quality Department is often considered to be another cost burden on the company and not one that could make a positive contribution towards the company profitability. Nothing could be further from the truth and the quality function is capable of making essential contributions towards the financial performance of the company. Not only from the point of view of making a quality product that consequently would secure a strong position in the marketplace for the company, but also by making significant savings in the overheads of the company.

Justification (Stage 1 - Sell)

It is essential to convince management of the need to investigate the cost of quality in order to gain their commitment and active participation to the cost of quality programme. The method of convincing management could be based on the following:

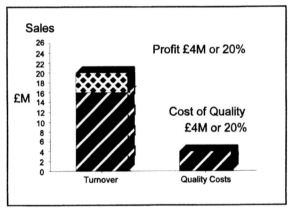

Figure 27

Consider a company with sales of £20M and making profits of 20%. Investigations into the cost of quality at a number of companies has shown that the cost of quality will typically lie between 5 and 25% of the company's turnover. (See **Figure 27**).

Now say a 50% improvement in profits is targeted i.e. £2M. The Overall Total Profit. Target = £6M To achieve this new target then one approach could be to

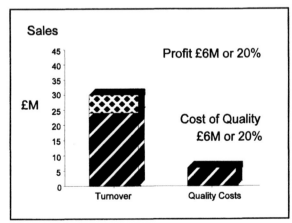

Figure 28

improve sales by a similar amount i.e. 50% providing the increased profit of £2M. **(See Figure 28)**.

Using this approach to achieve the targeted £6M profit will involve large financial investment together with a major expansion programme, obviously involving considerable risks, particularly if it is set against a background of fierce market competition.

There is, however, another approach, that is to reduce the cost of quality by 50% this will produce the same effect; saving £2M and meeting the target figure of £6M. (See **Figure 29**). Now it is worth considering which is the easier to achieve a further 50% market penetration or to reduce the cost of quality by 50%. Which of these two exercises would require the greater resource to accomplish?

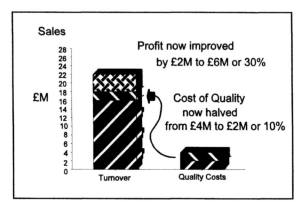

Figure 29

The answer would largely depend on the industry involved, but this exercise does give an indication of the saving that can be made without resorting to a major expansion programme with all its inherent risks. In fact there are no risks involved in trying to reduce quality costs other than committing resources to achieve the objective. So the Quality Department can have a major impact on the profitability and performance of the company. The concept that is being suggested is that going for the avoidable quality costs can have major benefits without major risks. How do we undertake an attack on the avoidable quality costs?

The following describes a quality cost reduction programme that could be employed:

Cost of Quality Reduction Programme

Stages in a Quality Cost Programme		
Stage	Name	Description
1	Sell	To establish whether it is viable to examine the cost of quality. Then to justify a programme to higher management to gain their commitment and agreement to provide allocation of resources.
2	Information	To find the key categories that go to make up the total quality cost.
3	Measurement	To assess the cost of each individual category and to decide how frequently the information should be gathered, together with establishing what resources should be allocated to gathering the data.
4	Analysis	To decide how the data will be analysed and when the results will be published and what form the results will take.
5	Action	To produce a programme that will effect a reduction in quality costs. Also to establish how this programme will be implemented and introduced including dates and targets.

Cost Of Quality

Quality cost categories: (Stage 2 - Information)

What are the major factors that go to make up the total cost of quality? Well, basically there are four, the next table explains each of the factors.

Cost of quality - definition

Quality Cost Categories	
Prevention Cost	The cost of action taken to examine, avoid or reduce the number of defects and failures.
Appraisal Cost	The cost of assessing the achieved quality standard.
Failure Cost: The cost arising as a result of failing to achieve the required quality standard, which can be broken down into internal and external failure.	
Internal Failure Cost	Internal failure being within the organisation (e.g. scrap).
External Failure Cost	External failure being outside the organisation (e.g. warranty claims). This cost has often been found to be by far the largest expenditure and can be as high as 90% of the cost of quality.

The proportion shown in the **Figure 30** typically reflects the expenditure or losses incurred against each category. The largest cost of quality is usually found to be failure costs, particularly warranty costs. The smallest cost of quality is usually prevention cost, the money spent on avoiding poor quality.

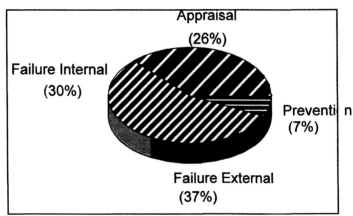

Figure 30

Introduction to Quality Assurance

The traditional approach to reducing the cost of quality was to attack the failure costs by increasing the appraisal costs (i.e. sorting the quality in). This would give the desired effect of stopping the customer receiving poor quality but has the knock on effect of increasing the internal failure costs (i.e. more scrap) and an increase in the appraisal costs (i.e. more inspectors). In order to break this cycle it is necessary to take preventive measures to stop the poor quality being produced in the first place, i.e. right first time.

So if the cost of quality is examined on the basis of prevention, appraisal and failure costs then this would assist in understanding the financial balance between these three factors. This information could be used in making judgements as to what the expenditure should be on prevention, appraisal and failure and to implement a cost reduction programme.

A typical company's cost of quality has been compiled. The break down of the costs can be seen in a spread sheet table. This table also shows some of the factors which are likely to make a contribution to the overall costs.
See Table - Spread Sheet showing Cost of Quality

Data collection (Stage 3 - measurement)

The cost of each of these categories now needs to be established. To accomplish this task it is often wise to elicit the assistance of the company accountant to review the list of categories and to advise, and in certain cases, obtain the required data.

Some data may not be readily available and some means of data collection could become necessary or in certain circumstances accurate estimating may be appropriate, such as in establishing the cost of any quality planning carried out by the design department.

Some of the data could be already available but not in a suitable format, e.g.

     i.   Staff and hourly paid payroll.
     ii.   Scrap reports.
     iii.   Rework reports.
     iv.   Customer returns and field service data etc.
     v.   Transport costs.
     vi.   Design change notes.

Cost Of Quality

The pound rule: It is worth spending a little time examining the cost of change as this can constitute a considerable amount of the cost of quality. If the cost of change is examined at each stage in a project then it can be seen that after each stage the cost of change will increase.

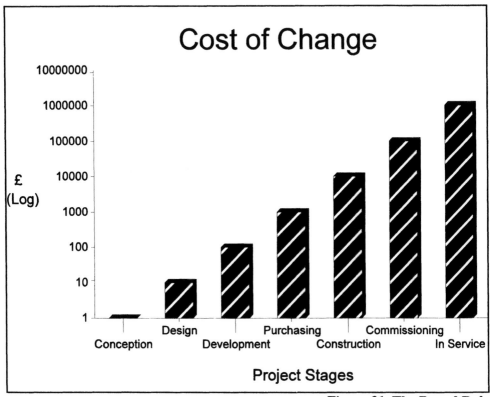

Figure 31 The Pound Rule

The change at the conceptual stage could only involve a few people and may require the rewriting of the functional specification - £1 (for an extremely simple change).

At the design stage a change could involve the redrawing of a number of drawings and possibly a rewrite to the specification - £10.

A change at the development stage could involve redrawing and further trials and tests - £100.

If the change occurs at the purchasing of equipment and material stage, this could involve extensive discussion with the supplier, changes to purchase orders and specification - £1000.

If construction or manufacturing has started and changes are required (possibly due to sub-assemblies not working or fitting together) then it can start to become extremely expensive, it may involve re-design and retesting of the new configuration - £10000.

At the commissioning stage changes may be required due to the product not passing the tests and trials. Man weeks of work may be required in resolving problems of making the product work satisfactorily and to customer requirements. A large investment has been made which cannot be recouped as the customer will not pay until the product works properly. In the worse case there may be penalty clauses for late delivery - £100,000.

In service and under warranty, if the product requires recall or a campaign change then the costs can be dramatic to the extent that companies become insolvent because of these excessive costs. Possibly the classic case of the cost of change is the Shuttle Challenger - £1,000,000.

The pound rule indicates that a pound invested at the start of a project could provide savings by a factor of 10 for each subsequent stage of the project.

Note, it may be considered that some of the estimated costs of change are very conservative.

Cost Of Quality

Table 6 Spread Sheet showing the Cost of Quality

Cost Category	Quarters				Total £K	Target £K	Diff £K
	Jan/Mar	Apr/Jun	Jul/Sep	Oct/Dec			
PREVENTION COSTS							
Quality Manag't & Sup'n	5031	5011	5039	5546	20.6	25	4.3
Quality Engineering	4258	4227	3935	3988	16.4	16	-0.4
Reliability Assessment	93	6	77	163	0.3	3	2.6
Audit	500	500	500	500	2	2	0
Supplier Assessment	636	590	424	16	1.7	3	1.3
Quality Training	437	265	250	586	1.5	5	3.5
Calibration	399	325	425	376	1.5	4	2.5
Equipment (Engineering)	990	288	515	1217	3	3	0
Total Prevention Costs	12344	11212	11165	12392	47	61	13.8
APPRAISAL COSTS							
Laboratory Accept Testing	48	52	16	463	0.6	1	0.4
In-Process Inspection	39336	39714	39201	39201	157.4	150	-7.4
Inspection & Test Equipment	2008	1916	776	402	5	12	6.9
Goods Receiving Inspection	4623	4590	4540	4548	18.3	20	1.7
Product Quality Audit	609	600	636	636	2.4	3	0.5
Total Appraisal Costs	46624	46872	45169	45250	183.7	186	2.1
INTERNAL FAILURE COSTS							
Scrap	33981	31947	22515	25533	11.4	100	-14
Rectification & Rework	14274	13056	12420	16695	56.4	50	-6.4
Cost of Change	3636	429	183	69	4.3	0	-4.3
Concessions	1530	348	135	42	20.5	0	-2.1
Total Internal Failure	53421	45780	35253	42339	92.6	150	-26.8
EXTERNAL FAILURE COSTS							
Warranty Returns	31076	34471	34805	33212	13.3	100	-33.5
Complaints	3732	3258	3065	3318	13	15	1.6
Product Liability	15000	0	0	0	15	15	0
Warranty Spares	15040	15289	15746	15460	6.2	50	-11.5
Total External Failure	64848	53018	53616	51990	47.5	180	-43.4
TOTAL COST OF QUALITY	177237	156882	145203	151971	370.8	577	-54.3
Sales Revenue	1004104	100151	1002477	1001791	4009	3600	-410

92

Introduction to Quality Assurance

Cost Category	Quarters				Total £K	Target £K	Diff £K
	Jan/Mar	Apr/Jun	Jul/Sep	Oct/Dec			
Manufacturing Costs	802575	810433	836565	835620	3285	4000	714.9
Direct Labour Costs	195686	187006	186888	180452	750	1200	450
% Cost of Quality/Sales	17.7%	15.7%	14.5%	15.2%	9.24%	16.0%	
% Scrap Cost/Manufactur'g	4.2%	3.9%	2.7%	3.1%	3.5%	2.5%	
% Rectif'n/Direct Labour	7.3%	7.0%	6.6%	9.3%	7.5%	4.2%	
% Warranty Returns/Sales	3.1%	3.4%	3.5%	3.3%	3.3%	2.8%	
% Warranty Spares/Sales	1.5%	1.5%	1.6%	1.5%	1.5%	1.4%	

Investigation (Stage 4 - Analysis)

Having identified the cost of each of the categories then these costs need to be analysed as a prelude to taking action to reduce the total cost. The analysis can be accomplished by various methods:

1. Comparison between prevention, appraisal and failure costs.

This provides the first snapshot of the way by which quality is organised and gives an initial guide as to whether the right balance is being maintained between prevention and appraisal.

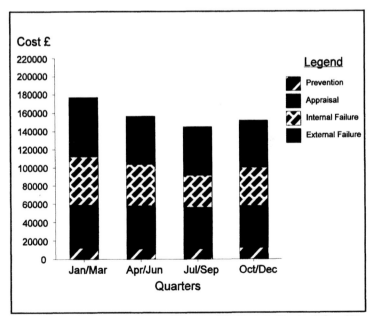

Figure 32 Total Cost of Quality

93

2. Comparison by time.

Analysis of quality cost data on the basis of time is essential in indicating trends, monitoring performance and to ascertain whether real improvements are being made reducing the cost of quality.

3. Comparison between products or departments.

The cost data can also be arranged by product or department to enable comparisons to be made between the relative performance of one product with another, or one department with another.

a. Bases.

The cost figures by themselves indicate the expenditure on quality however to establish a true and consistent guide as to the relative costs it is necessary to relate the costs to different bases or indices.

Some examples of quality cost indices can be:

(1) Labour hours - Number of personnel involved in production or direct labour hours.

$$\% \; Rectification \; = \; \frac{Rectification \; Hours \; x \; 100\%}{Direct \; Labour \; Hours}$$

The comparison of rectification hours is based on the time spent on rectifying bad products against the time spent on making products. This comparison could be demonstrated graphically showing the year's percentage rectification performance.

$$\% \; Cost \; of \; Appraisal \; = \; \frac{Inspection \; Hours \; + \; Test \; Hours \; Hours \; x \; 100\%}{Direct \; Labour \; Hours}$$

The cost of appraisal is a comparison of the time spent making the product against the time spent inspecting and testing the product.

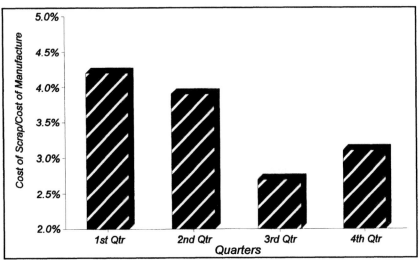

Figure 33   Percentage Scrap

i.   Quantity - Number of components produced.

$$\% \ Scrap \ = \ \frac{Number \ of \ Components \ Scrapped \ x \ 100\%}{Number \ of \ Components \ Produced}$$

The percentage scrap calculation compares the number of bad components made against the number of good components made. (Sometimes referred to as yield).

$$\% \ Warranty \ Returns \ = \ \frac{Number \ of \ Warranty \ Returns \ x \ 100\%}{Total \ Number \ of \ Products \ Sold}$$

The calculation of percentage warranty compares the number of products returned faulty with the number of products sold and provides some indication of the changes in the proportion of warranty returns.

ii.   Costs

■   Value of the output (unaffected by the fluctuation in sales).
■   Manufacturing cost (labour + material costs).
■   Value of the sales.

Cost Of Quality

$$\% \ Total \ Cost \ of \ Quality \ = \ \frac{Total \ Cost \ of \ Quality \ x \ 100\%}{Value \ of \ the \ Output}$$

The total cost of quality calculation compares the money spent on quality against the value of the output. The diagram *Total Cost of Quality* shows the changes in the percentage total cost of quality throughout the year, together with the proportion of the costs spend on prevention, appraisal and failure. This diagram also shows the changes in the proportions of prevention, appraisal and failure.

Optimum quality

According to the PAF[10] model of the cost of quality model there is an economic limit to quality improvement. There comes a point where the cost of prevention is greater than the savings made by the reduction of defects. However, this is based on purely financial grounds and there may be other more important considerations such as risk to life.

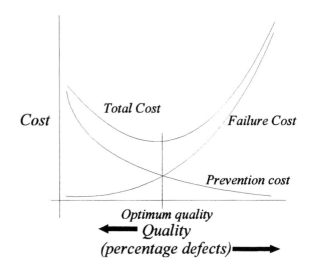

Figure 34

---

[10]   Prevention, Appraisal, Failure BS6143 Part 2

PART B

Quality in Design

Quality in Design

Introduction

A product can only be as good as its design. If the design is wrong a perfect craftsman would make a perfectly wrong product.

The quality of design is how well the designer has interpreted the customer's requirements and translated them into instructions for manufacture.

The extent of the design activity must not be underestimated but it often is. Many people associate design with *styling* of products. The aesthetic consideration is certainly an important aspect, but for certain products and many service operations the other *design* considerations are vital. For example, anyone who has bought an 'assemble-it-yourself' kitchen unit will know the importance of the design of the assembly instructions. Aspects of design that affect quality in this way are packaging, customer service arrangements, maintenance routines, warranty details and their fulfilment, spare part availability, etc.

Many common causes of customer dissatisfaction have not been product features but problems with user manuals, availability, compatibility and loading of software, and applications. For technically complex products or service systems, the design and marketing of after-sales arrangements are an essential component of the design activity. The design of production equipment and its layout to allow ease of access for repair and essential maintenance, or simple use as intended, widens the management of design quality into suppliers and contractors and requires their total commitment.

Proper design of systems, goods and equipment plays a major role in the elimination of errors, defectives and waste. Correct initial design also obviates the need for costly and wasteful modifications to be carried out after equipment has been manufactured. It is at the design stage that such important matters as variability, reproducibility, ease of use in operations, maintainability, etc., should receive detailed consideration.

Designing

Quality design is taking care of all aspects of the customer's requirements, including cost, production, safe and easy use, and maintainability of products and services. Hence, *designing* must take place in all aspects of: reliability, maintainability, interchangeability, standardisation, productivity, safety and environmental matters.

Design includes all aspects, from the identification of a problem to be solved, usually a market need, through the development of design concepts and prototypes to the generation of detailed specifications or instructions required to produce the artefact or provide the service. It is the process of presenting needs in some physical form, initially as a solution, and then as a specific configuration or arrangement of materials, resources, equipment, and people.

Figure 35 indicates, a typical procedure for the introduction of a new design showing the role of design in relation to other activities.

Quality in Design

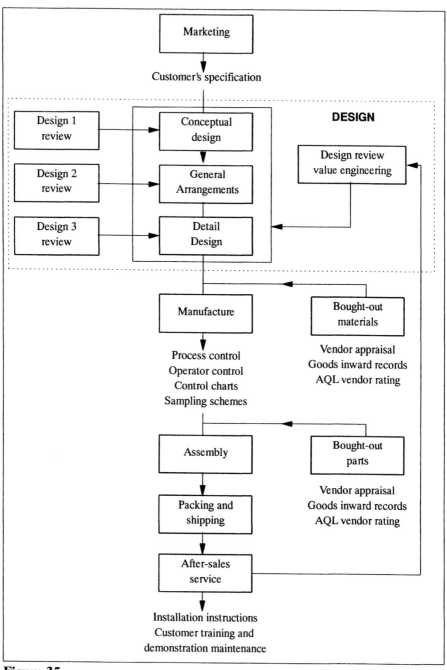

Figure 35

Design control and management

Design as with any other activity, must be carefully managed. A flow chart of the various stages and activities involved in the design and development process appear in the next diagram.

Quality in Design

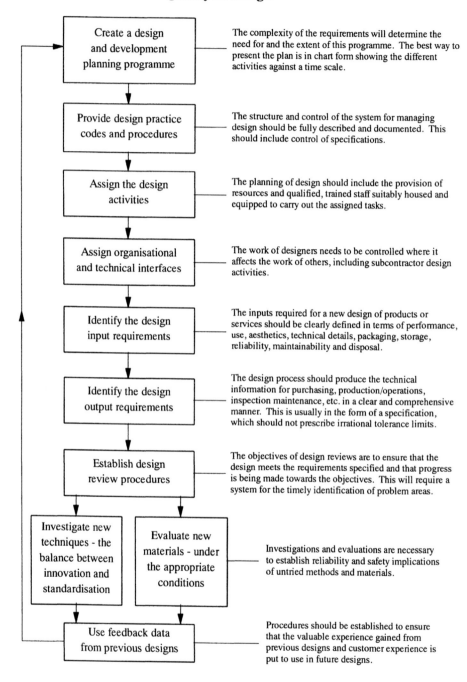

Figure 36

Introduction to Quality Assurance

Some of these steps may need the support of the Quality Department. For example, design codes may need checking for conformity to best practice; product standards may need to comply with industry or regulatory standards, and so on. In addition, the Quality Department may need to approve any specific quality planning for this particular product, especially if it is different from existing products.

By structuring the design process in this way, it is possible to:

- Control the various stages.
- Check that they have been completed.
- Decide which management functions need to be brought in and at what stage.
- Estimate the level of resources needed.

The design control must be carefully handled to avoid stifling the creativity of the designer, which is crucial in making design solutions a reality.

It is clear that the design process requires a range of specialised skills and the way in which these skills are managed. The way these skills interact, and the amount of effort devoted to the different stages of the design and development process, is fundamental to the quality, producibility and the price of the service or final product.

The Economics of Quality Design

Value Analysis and Value Engineering

Strictly speaking Value Engineering is a systematic method of examining *new* products, systems, or services aimed at improving cost-effectiveness. It relates to the development of new products whereas Value Analysis (VA) relates to the analysis of *existing* product systems or services. Frequently they are taken to mean the same thing.

In the previous units, it has been shown how investment at the early stages of design can yield greater benefits at later stages. VA studies will cost money. However, it is not unreasonable to expect a return of 15:1 that is for every £1 spent on the analysis £15 is saved. At least a 10:1 return should be the aim.

Introduction

The aim of Value Analysis or Engineering is to investigate the function of a system, process or equipment with the objective of achieving the intended function at the lowest overall cost. The technique is a logical, disciplined approach that can be applied from individual components or stages up to complete systems or processes. It consists of five basic phases:

(1) Information phase
(2) Function phase
(3) Speculation phase
(4) Evaluation phase
(5) Implementation phase

Sometimes, when systems or products are designed, certain key customer requirements can be overlooked. Also, not all the design options may have been considered. VA provides the opportunity for a team of people to review critically the system or product design to establish simpler, cheaper and more effective ways of achieving the design's intended function. This technique has provided some astounding successes in reducing the design and manufacturing costs. Savings of tens of thousands of pounds per month is not unusual. It is particularly successful when the system or product has never been subject to Value Analysis before.

Procedure

Value Analysis is a team approach, although the first stage, i.e information, may be completed by one person, subsequent stages requires a team effort.

Information Phase:
This phase involves gaining as much information as possible about the item under evaluation to enable a complete understanding of the system being studied. This can include: obtaining drawings and parts lists, diagrams and photographs, descriptions of the process, flow diagrams, customer specifications, costs, budgets, time scales or quantities. It may be that some of this information is sketchy or unavailable. This phase can be a very lengthy stage (100 man hours are not unusual). See **Table 7**.

Table 7 Information Form

INFORMATION PHASE	
Basic Data	Information
Title Drawing Number and Issue No.	
Design Data Design Material Quantity	
Process Data Process Costs Volumes/batch sizes	Materials Labour Sub-Contract

Function phase: This phase involves defining the basic function of the item under evaluation.

The function is the purpose for which the item exists, the very reason for which it was designed and manufactured. This can be broken down into two parts; the basic and secondary function.

The basic function is the specific feature which must be attained. It may be that the item has two basic functions to perform.

Whereas secondary function includes the features which are other than those which must be attained. It is helpful to express the function of the item in terms of a verb and a noun. This ensures an exact understanding and statement of the function of the item, which provides the opportunity for exploring many possible approaches to achieving the function. (See **Table 8**)

Table 8 Function Form

Information Purpose		
What does the item do? Operation & Performance Is this task necessary Can another method or component perform this function		
Function Basic Secondary	Verb	Noun
Are all these functions necessary		
Other major design requirements / constraints		

Table 9 shows this function definition. Using a screw driver as an example the basic function is to convey torque (including the handle) and the secondary function is to aid friction. If the screw driver were an electrician's screw driver then another basic function would be to protect the user/electrician.

Table 9 Basic Function

Function	Verb	Noun
Basic Function	Conveys	Torque
Secondary Function	Aids	Friction

Speculation phase: This phase involves speculating about as many problem solutions as possible. Often this phase is called Brain Storming. Brain Storming can be used to generate possible solutions and subsequentially, to develop possible action plans.

Brain Storming

Table 10 Evaluation Form

Initially, a full understanding of the function of the item will have been gained by the completion of the information and function phases. When the function has been clearly stated, the next stage is for the team to propose as many different solutions as possible. To get accustomed to the concept of brain storming it may be helpful for the team to brain storm a trivial problem such as "What are the different

Evaluation Phase		
Possible Solution	Advantages	Disadvantages

uses of a brick?" before moving on to the actual problem. It is important that this speculation is performed freely with no evaluation or criticism of the proposed solutions or approaches. During the brain storm all of the team's suggestions are written on a flip chart with the objective that the team may develop other ideas.

Evaluation phase: Having generated a list of possible solutions, these solutions require evaluation to determine the most appropriate approach.

Quality in Design

The list of solutions is initially reviewed to remove ones which can obviously be rejected. Next, the list is rewritten and the team award marks for each suggestion in terms of cost, simplicity, ease of application and introduction. A scale of 1 to 10 can be used. For example:

Highest cost award 1, lowest cost award 10
Most complex award 1, most simple award 10
Difficult to implement award 1, easy to implement award 10

These numbers can be multiplied together to give an overall score for each suggestion.

This should reduce the list down to the final few where upon the Evaluation Form can be employed. Each of the remaining solutions is listed on the left-hand side of the form. On the right-hand side each solution's good and bad features are listed, e.g. costs (material and manufacturing) etc.

At this stage, other information may be required (costings, feasibility studies etc.) and action may need to be taken away from the VA team's meeting. (See table Approvals Form).

At any time during the evaluation phase, it may be appropriate to return to the speculation phase to refine some of the ideas but it is important to remember not to criticise or evaluate while speculating.

Implementation phase: This is probably the most difficult of all the phases discussed but the most important as the value analysis team has not completed its task until the proposed solution has been implemented. There will be numerous reasons or negative attitudes, put forward as

Table 11 Approvals Form

Implementation Phase		
Features	Proposed	Current
Cost Analysis Material Cost Labour Cost Sub-contract Cost		
Implementation Cost Detailed Design Product Development Equipment Design & Manufacture Other Costs		
Approvals Quality Purchasing Design Marketing Customer Service Production		

to why the proposed solution will not work or not be acceptable. "We've done it before"; "the customer won't accept it", "too difficult", "too expensive" etc. All of these problems need to be addressed before implementation can be achieved. Many

Table 12 Implementation Form

Implementation Phase		
Stage	**Date**	**Duration**
Submit VA proposals		
Approve VA proposals		
Produce Specification		
Review & Approve specification		
Design FMECA		
Produce prototype		
Test prototype (Lab & field)		
Produce process plan		
Process FMECA		
Produce Inspection & test plan		
Process Approval		
Purchase items		
Process capability studies		
Produce		

key people will need to be convinced of the viability of the proposed solution.

An Approvals Form (see **Table - Approvals Form**) is one method of clearly listing the benefits gained by the implementation of the solution. The Approval Form can also be used to record acceptance of the approach by the relevant personnel.

A clear implementation programme is required and again the brain storming techniques can be employed. Implementation Form (see **Table - Implementation Form**) may be used to provide guidance in establishing the Implementation Programme.

Quality in Design

Table 13 Check List

Area	Questions
Product Function	1. What are the basic functions? 2. What are the secondary functions? 3. Are all the functions necessary? 4. What else will perform the same function? 5. Can any of the functions be incorporated in other components?
Materials	1. What material is used? 2. What is the material specification? 3. Can any other material be used? 4. Can any other specification of the same material be used? 5. Can waste material be reduced? 6. Can raw material be standardised? 7. Can raw material be obtained in a different form? 8. What is the price of the material? 9. What indirect materials are used? (e.g. packing, lubrication, etc.) 10. Can pre-finished materials be used?
Size and Specification	1. Can dimensions be reduced? 2. Is the part oversize? 3. If less expensive material is used can size be increased? 4. What tolerances are specified? 5. Which tolerances are not critical? (e.g. may selective assembly or statistical tolerancing techniques be considered?) 6. Can tolerances be increased? 7. Can a standard part be used? 8. What finish is required? 9. Are the finish standards essential? 10. Can an alternative method of applying the finish be used? 11. Is the product range too great?
Manufacture	1. Can any operations be eliminated or changed. (E.g. cast v machined v forged v all welded.) 2. Can any operations be combined? 3. Can any operations be simplified? 4. Would a different material simplify manufacture? 5. Can standard processes be used? 6. Can standard tools and jigs be used? 7. Can assembly operations be reduced? 8. Can pre-fabricated parts be used? 9. Would it be cheaper to buy the parts?

Failure Mode Effects and Criticality Analysis

Introduction

Failure Mode Effects & Criticality Analysis (FMECA) is a logical technique used to identify and eliminate possible causes of failure. The technique requires a sequential, disciplined approach by a team to assess systems, products or processes in order to establish the modes of failure and the effects of failure on the system, product or process. This is to ensure that all possible failure modes have been fully identified and ranked in order of their importance.

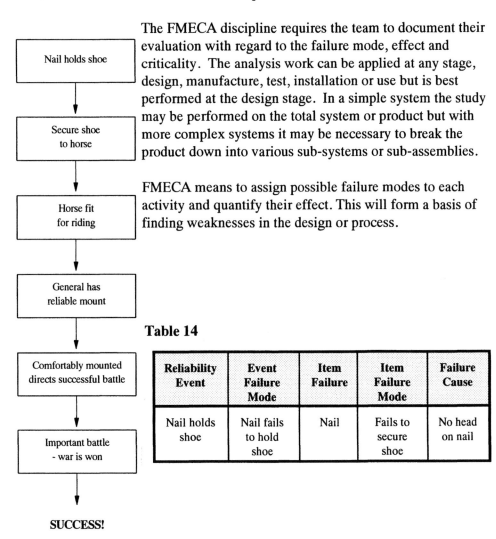

The FMECA discipline requires the team to document their evaluation with regard to the failure mode, effect and criticality. The analysis work can be applied at any stage, design, manufacture, test, installation or use but is best performed at the design stage. In a simple system the study may be performed on the total system or product but with more complex systems it may be necessary to break the product down into various sub-systems or sub-assemblies.

FMECA means to assign possible failure modes to each activity and quantify their effect. This will form a basis of finding weaknesses in the design or process.

Table 14

Reliability Event	Event Failure Mode	Item Failure	Item Failure Mode	Failure Cause
Nail holds shoe	Nail fails to hold shoe	Nail	Fails to secure shoe	No head on nail

In FMECA all possible failures must be identified. The consequence of failure produces the FMECA. This analysis gives the designer ideas and comparisons at the superficial level on the first run. Further Analysis down to the smallest levels may be done on high risks taken.

Table 15

Effect on sub system	Effect on system		Preventive Action	
	Reliability	**Safety**	**Design**	**QA**
Horse goes lame	Horse unfit for battle, General unable to direct battle ➜ War Lost!	Officer dislodged from seat	Use more nails	Check quality of nails

The reason for FMECA

With ever increasing demands to ensure that QUALITY is achieved **RIGHT FIRST TIME** then still greater pressures are placed on the Design Engineer. This is to ensure that the Engineer's design performs consistently, reliably and safely throughout the life of the product, thus providing a quality product that completely meets the demands of the customer. Designers are only human and they can make mistakes and have off days just like everyone else. FMECA ensures that any inadequacies in the design are quickly identified, preventing the possibility of releasing sub-standard products. Product testing will, of course, help identify any design deficiencies.

There are, however, possible limitations with this approach:

- If the product fails the trial, then the modified and hopefully improved design will need to be re-tested - this can lead to inefficient use of resource.

Introduction to Quality Assurance

- Tests and trials can usually only be performed on a limited number of products, consequently all the possible variations in specification and build standard cannot always be evaluated. Using small samples may also not be sufficiently accurate to predict field failure rates, particularly when attempting to identify causes of potentially low field failure rates. These missed potential failures may result in the need for product recall or the issuing of advisory notices, (particularly in the case of safety critical failures). This can be not only expensive but also damaging for both the company and product's credibility and reputation.

FMECA provides the potential for:

- Reducing the likelihood of service failures
- Reducing the chance of campaign changes
- Reducing maintenance and warranty costs
- Reducing the possibility of safety failures
- Reducing the potential of extended life failures
- Reducing the likelihood of Product Liability claims

With FMECA the emphasis is on removal of the likely cause of any potential failures. However FMECA can also indicate to the engineer the features in the design which require sophisticated quality control monitoring, possibly with the use of Statistical Quality Control (see section on Statistical Quality Control).

Responsibility for FMECA

The analysis can be performed by either the design, manufacturing or quality engineer but the most suitable is the person or team who knows the system, product or process best. The design is the person most likely to conduct this analysis as having the complete knowledge of the product and therefore can best anticipate the failure mode and the effect of the failure modes. The FMECA technique can be completed by an individual but is best carried out as a team exercise led by the engineer responsible for the product or sub-assembly. The team could include the designer, quality engineer, manufacturing engineer, customer and where appropriate any sub-contractors.

Some benefits of the application of FMECA can be:

- Identifying potential and known failures.
- Identifying the cause and effect of such a failure mode.
- Ranking the identified failure modes in terms of risk factor.
- Following up or taking action on the potential failure modes.

Failure Mode Effects and Criticality Analysis

- Providing detailed documentation for the purpose of quality audit.
- Checking on the FMECA decisions in the event of a major failure.
- Making clear the accountability for the system, product or process.

Limitations of FMECA

FMECA involves a considerable amount of time and labour resource in performing the study but in any case this is only time that would need to be spent in order to evaluate satisfactorily the design. Conducting an FMECA does require the completion of paperwork but at the end of the analysis documentary evidence is available proving an assessment was performed. Even after completing an FMECA, it may be that the key design failures may have been overlooked by the team and failures still occur. However the likelihood of such an event has been reduced. It may also be that after completing the FMECA, no action will be taken regarding the potential failures that have been identified. This may be the case but clear responsibilities for taking action will have been established.

FMECA procedure

The key stages in any failure mode and effects analysis on a design, product, system or process are detailed below and should be followed in conjunction with the FMECA form shown at the end of this section.

(1) Logistics

The system, sub-system, item or process and the FMECA team members need to be selected. All the relevant information needs to be collated: samples, drawings, customer brief, field failure information etc.

(2) Header details

Complete the details at the top of the form including name of the engineer who performed the study and is responsible for the design. Include the revision status of the drawing and the FMECA. *Note, if the study was performed by a team then the name of the team leader.*

(3) Part, process or system name and number

Complete details regarding the part, process or system name and number.

(4) Describe the function

The team must identify as briefly as possible the function of the part, component or the system being analysed. The question needed to be asked is: "What is the purpose of this part?"

(5) Describe the anticipated failure mode

The team must consider how this part could fail to complete its intended function? For example, could it break, bind, corrode, wear, deform, leak, short, etc. It is important at this stage that the team should be asking the question: "How could it fail?" not whether or not it will fail.

(6) Describe the effects of failure

The team must describe what the effects of failure on the final component or the assembly. The question: "What will happen as a result of the failure mode described?" needs to be posed. Will the component or assembly be inoperative, intermittent or noisy, inefficient, not durable, inaccurate etc.?

(7) Cause - describe the cause of failure

Anticipation as to the cause of failure is necessary at this stage. What is being sought is that set of conditions or factors can bring about the failure mode? For example:.

- Could a foreign body jam the mechanism?
- Would poor or wrong material cause the mechanism to break?
- Would poor soldering cause the wire to short or cause an open circuit?
- Is there non-compliance with specifications or are specifications unachievable?

The team must analyse what conditions could bring about the failure mode.

(8) Estimate the frequency of occurrence of the failure

Here it is necessary to estimate the probability that a failure mode will occur. This estimation will be evaluated on a scale of 1 to 10. A number 1 would indicate a very low probability of occurrence, 10 would indicate near certainty of occurrence. The team needs to assess the probability of an occurrence based on their knowledge and experience of the product. The following evaluation scale may be used as a guide.

1	=	1 in 1,000,000 chance of occurrence
2 and 3	=	1 in 100,000 chance of occurrence
4 and 5	=	1 in 10,000 chance of occurrence
6 and 7	=	1 in 1,000 chance of occurrence
8	=	1 in 100 chance of occurrence
9	=	1 in 10 chance of occurrence
10	=	100% chance of occurrence

(9) Estimate the severity of failure

At this stage, it is necessary to determine the likely severity of failure and again the scale of 1 to 10 is used, where a number 1 would indicate a minor nuisance and 10 would indicate severe consequences such as fatality or serious damage to property. An estimate must be made of the severity of the failure. The team must consider the consequence of failure using the following severity scale as a guide:

1	=	unlikely to be detected
2	=	25% chance of service call
3	=	50% chance of service call
4	=	75% chance of service call
5	=	100% chance of service call
6	=	failure on installation or first use
7	=	failure results in customer complaint
8	=	failure results in a serious customer complaint
9	=	failure results in a fire, accident or injury
10	=	failure results in noncompliance with statutory safety standard or a fatality

(10) Estimate the probability of detection of failure

An estimate must be made of the probability that a potential failure will be detected before it reaches a customer. Again the evaluation scale of 1 to 10 is used. A number 1 would indicate a very high probability that failure would be detected before reaching the customer and 10 would indicate a very low probability that the failure would be detected in-house and, therefore, is likely to be experienced by the customer. For example, if a 100% conclusive test is performed on the component, it is unlikely that the fault will reach the customer and is, thereof, assigned a number 1. Alternatively, if no checks are performed then it is highly likely that, if faulty, the defective product will reach the customer and is, therefore, assigned 10.

1 = failure will be detected
2 = 80% chance of detection
3 = 70% chance of detection
4 = 60% chance of detection
5 = 50% chance of detection
6 = 40% chance of detection
7 = 30% chance of detection
8 = 20% chance of detection
9 = 10% chance of detection
10 = no chance of detection

(11) Calculate the risk priority number

By multiplying together the assessed likelihood of occurrence, the severity and the likelihood of detection, the risk priority number (rpn) is found. The highest number being 1000, the smallest number being 1. From this number it is possible to determine which are the high priority items in terms of failure mode. The higher the risk number the more critical is the component or item failure.

(12) Determine corrective action

The basic purpose of failure mode and effects analysis is to highlight the potential failure mode so that the team can take steps to eliminate or reduce the risk. At this stage, it is necessary to analyse the risk number and determine what appropriate action is necessary. Obviously a high risk number would indicate immediate action whereas a low risk number may be ignored or could require some minor checks to be included.

(13) Follow up

Having determined what the appropriate corrective action should be it is now necessary to perform a further FMECA to ensure that the resulting risk number has been reduced to an acceptable risk. It is also advisable to confirm at some later date that the proposed action has been successfully and effectively implemented.

Failure Mode Effects and Criticality Analysis

Table 16 FMECA Form

Product: Component Name: Component Number: Revision Number: Effect of Purchasing: Yes/No					Engineer or Team: Dates: Report Number: Sheet of Sheets: Revision Number: Last Updated:				
Part, Process or System & Number	Function	Possible Failure Mode	Effect of Failure	Cause of Failure	Occurrence	Severity	Detection	Risk	Remarks/ Action Taken

Rationalisation of Product Range - Variety Reduction

Introduction

In the West there is a tremendous range of choice. The average shoe shop carries hundreds of shoes having different styles, colours, heels, shapes and sizes, etc. The same may be said for clothes, cars, furnishings and modern table tennis bats. The late Eastern block countries have had very little choice, or 'Hobson's Choice' as it were, i.e. take it or leave it. Our planet seems to have two entirely different groups - the haves and the have nots.

The question really is, do we have too much choice? The answer to this is complicated by market forces. With no competition around, manufacturers can afford to offer very limited choice. With a limited range of colours, styles, shapes and sizes etc. the product should be cheaper, but in a seller's market, this breeds inefficiency and contempt for the customer. The rust traps produced by the UK car manufacturers in the fifties and sixties are prime examples of this.

With competition, the customer expects more from the products on display - a buyer's market usually results in discounts and rock bottom prices. This happy state will not last long as companies go out of business, leaving only the efficient and quality conscious ones. The problem with choice is that it makes individual products more expensive, and in the long run the customer pays for variety.

In a practical sense, which is from a strictly engineering point of view, rationalisation of a product range, with its subsequent reduction of choice, or variety reduction as it is called, may be an extremely useful exercise.

When pots of paint are being produced there is little point in having them available in an arithmetic series, e.g. say 0.25, 0.5, 0.75, 1, 1.25, 1.50, 1.75, 2, litres etc., as this gives us far too much choice. Market share will not fall if the available range is 0.25, 0.5, 1, 2, 4 litres etc., certainly the absence of some of the can sizes should cheapen the range, as manufacturing packaging and storage costs will not be so high as a result of this reduction. This second series is geometric, each subsequent value being a specific multiple of the previous value.

Rationalisation of Product Range

Similarly, fastening devices such as screws, nuts and bolts, rivets etc., may be made in various diameters, lengths, heads, etc., and it could be that reductions in this choice are a possibility. The single criteria, in this instance, is that the reduction in the choice will not affect quality or reliability. The test is whether the customer will notice and rect to the reduction in such choice. If not, then economies can be made.

Such reductions in costs may be the result of VALUE ANALYSIS, which all efficient, economically minded manufacturers will subscribe to.

Size ranges

The advantages of standard ranges are lost if too many graduations of size occur within a specified range. For Example a size range of electric motors might contain a 500 watt and 750 watt size at the lower end, i.e. a 50% increase, and such a range is also likely to include a 5 kw and 7½kw motor, which again is an increase of 50%. It would be an unnecessary duplication of sizes to include a 5¼kw motor in the range - which will mean a 5% increase. The manufacturers of large quantities of each size in a limited size range will enable motors to be supplied at a lower price than if a wider choice were given. The full economic advantages of quality manufacturing methods can thus be exploited. Similar reasoning can be applied to the dimensional aspects of many products, e.g. diameters of bolts, drills, reamers, the thickness of steel sheet, the values of resistors and capacitors, the limits and fits system (as defined in BS 4500) and the speeds of machine tools etc.

A rational series of standard sizes will tend to follow a geometric series

a, ar, ar^2, ar^3 ---- $ar^{(n-1)}$ where r is the constant rate of increase, n is the number in the series, e.g. 1, 2, 4, 8, 16 -------.

Many standard sizes have been arrived at empirically, e.g. BS Whitworth threads, and do not follow geometric rates of increase exactly, but the closeness of agreement is surprising; in fact, the imperial length system is exactly based on a geometric progression with a ratio of 2

i.e. $\dfrac{1"}{64}$ $\dfrac{1"}{32}$ $\dfrac{1"}{16}$ $\dfrac{1"}{8}$ $\dfrac{1"}{4}$ $\dfrac{1"}{2}$ -----

However, the sizes of new products should be related to an agreed series of numbers in order to avoid unnecessary duplication and to obtain maximum advantages of standardisation. BS 2045 presents a basis for selecting preferred number series. (See Extract from BS 2045 : 1965).

Products of quite different types and origins may also have certain factors in common that would be desirable to correlate. For example the designer of a series of power driven pumps might conceivably assign capacities to them which did not conform to the powers of motors commercially available. In the case of two newly developing industries it is quite possible that such divergencies might arise, involving wasteful use of one or other product. On the other hand, if both designers work to the schedule of preferred numbers, it is at least probable that such difficulties will be in large measure overcome in advance.

It is patently obvious that a certain degree of commonsense must be applied in selecting a range using the preferred series that is available. Parts of the standard RENARD (see below) number series may be selected to suit requirements, values being rounded up or down for simplicity.

Rationalisation of Product Range

Extract from BS 2045 : 1965

BASIC SERIES OF PREFERRED NUMBERS

1	2	3	4	5
Serial number	**Basic series**			
	R5	R10	R20	R40
123	1	1	1.00 1.12	1.00 1.06 1.12 1.18
4567		1.25	1.25 1.40	1.25 1.32 1.40 1.50
891011	1.6	1.6	1.60 1.80	1.60 1.70 1.80 1.90
12131415		2	2.00 2.24	2.00 2.12 2.24 2.36
16171819	2.5	2.5	2.50 2.80	2.50 2.65 2.80 3.00
20212223		3.15	3.15 3.55	3.15 3.35 3.55 3.75
24252627	4	4	4.00 4.50	4.00 4.25 4.50 4.75
28293031		5	5.00 5.60	5.00 5.30 5.60 6.00
32333435	6.3	6.3	6.30 7.10	6.30 6.70 7.10 7.50
36373839		8	8.00 9.00	8.00 8.50 9.00 9.50
40	10	10	10	10

Introduction to Quality Assurance

Preferred Numbers

Preferred numbers are a series of numbers which are selected for the purpose of standardisation and simplification, in preference to other numbers. The idea of preferred numbers was first introduced by Colonel Charles Renard in 1870, and is sometimes referred to as the Renard series. He was faced with a simplification problem because 425 different sizes of cable were used in his army unit. In carrying out a process of standardisation in order to reduce the range of sizes, he suggested that a geometric series should be used as a basis of selection. His series is shown below, the series being denoted by an 'R'.

Renard series of preferred numbers

Series	Ratio	Steps increase by
R5	$\sqrt[5]{10} = 1.58$	60%
R10	$\sqrt[10]{10} = 1.26$	25%
R20	$\sqrt[20]{10} = 1.12$	12%
R40	$\sqrt[40]{10} = 1.06$	6%
R80	$\sqrt[80]{10} = 1.03$	3%

Many standard size ranges for products such as sheet steel, drawn wire, bolts, etc., will be found to follow a geometric series.

Example

A manufacturer wishes to produce a range of refrigerators. The range has to include six models; the smallest to have a cabinet capacity of $0.06m^3$. Calculate the range of sizes if they are to rise in geometric progression.

Solution

The R5 series can be used, this being a geometric progression of the form:

a, ar, ar^2, ar^3, ar^4 and ar^5 having six terms and five steps, where a is the first term, and r is the rate of increase of the steps.

Rationalisation of Product Range

In the R5 series, $r = \sqrt[5]{10} = 1.585$

Therefore the range of sizes will be:

First size	=	$0.06m^3$		
Second size	=	0.06×1.585	=	0.095 say $0.10m^3$
Third size	=	$0.06 \times (1.585)^2$	=	$0.15m^3$
Fourth size	=	$0.06 \times (1.585)^3$	=	0.239 say $0.24m^3$
Fifth size	=	$0.06 \times (1.585)^4$	=	0.378 say $0.38m^3$
Sixth size	=	$0.06 \times (1.585)^5$	=	$0.6m^3$

If the R10 series were used, then the range of sizes would start at $0.06m^3$ rising in 10 steps to $0.60m^3$. The R80 series gives 80 steps, such a large range as this rarely being used in practice. Of course, only part of a series may be used if required.

Economic Aspects of Preferred Sizes

The justification for using preferred numbers in a programme of standardisation and simplification is that unnecessary overlapping of sizes is eliminated. In the example, the product sizes rise in steps of approximately 60%, and it would appear to add unnecessary variety to the range to include yet a further size of $0.13m^3$ say, in that 0.13 overlaps the 0.1 and 0.15 sizes. The addition of such an extra model could be economically unsound, because high production of a narrow range of products can be carried out more cheaply than the production of a wider range of products.

There is, however, another side to this argument. Imagine that the refrigerator manufacturer of the example used an existing range of seven models; the R5 series plus the 0.13 model. He wishes to simplify the range in order to reduce his manufacturing costs and probably reduce his prices. If the preferred series becomes the criterion, then the 0.13 model must be eliminated. However, this may be the most popular model in the range to the customer, and the most profitable model to the firm; therefore to eliminate it from the range would appear to be wrong. Again, it may be that the wholesaler has an occasional demand from the retailers for a 'special 0.13' model, which cannot be obtained from any other source. Therefore, the wholesaler takes a good proportion of the standard models, which may not be the best on the market, from the manufacturer, in order to keep up the supply of the 0.13 model which he cannot otherwise obtain.

Introduction to Quality Assurance

Economic considerations are rarely straightforward and simple and it is therefore imperative that a programme of simplification is carried out using accurate and careful cost analysis. Valuable information can be obtained using a break-even chart for each product in the range, plotting total sales income (£) against total costs (£). This establishes the break-even point between profit and loss for each model.

Prototype Testing

Introduction

At the prototype or pilot-production stage one, a few, or a pilot production run, depending on the complexity of the item, of the product will be built. These are not for sale, but for assessment of the product and the processes that will be used to produce it. Before the design is finalised and approved for production, data gained from the prototypes must be used to verify that the product will conform to its safety standards.

An important aspect of prototype testing is field trials. Testing against the relevant standards and specifications is effective but limited to the features they cover. These may not be as complete as you expect, and testing in live conditions is a valuable further check. However, the tests must be chosen carefully to reflect the full range of conditions in which the final product will be used. Effective testing also means the close involvement of the purchaser, the end-users and other 'stakeholders' in defining, preparing, executing and evaluating the tests. Incidentally, when field trials have been completed, it is important to make sure that the test environment is restored to its pre-trial state.

When the prototype proved to be fit for production, the design is frozen and placed under 'configuration control'. Production for sale can then commence. Thereafter, the product will typically be tested before release and its overall performance reappraised periodically by more detailed tests on a sample.

Any further changes in the process or product specification which seem desirable in the light of production experience may only be introduced under the discipline of a formal engineering change procedure. These disciplines will continue to safeguard the safety provisions as well as all other aspects of product quality.

Configuration Control

The commonly used expression 'configuration control', 'modification control', or 'baseline control', implies control of design details whether recorded on paper or on magnetic media. Configuration is defined as: 'The complete description of the product and the relationship of its constituent elements'. A particular approved configuration at a specific point in time acts as a 'configuration baseline'.

Introduction to Quality Assurance

'Configuration control' is:

The discipline that ensures that any proposed change, addition, modification or amendment to the configuration baseline shall be prepared, accepted and controlled in accordance with set procedures.

Reliability

Introduction

Reliability is the time dependent measurement of quality. Products leaving the production line may be inspected for defects or deviations from specified requirements. However, there may be weaknesses which have not been determined by final inspection. In addition, weaknesses may have been introduced during packaging, despatch and installation.   What is more, products deteriorate during use and eventually wear out. Thus reliability is quality in service.

Definition::

The ability of an item or system to perform a required function under stated conditions for a stated period of time.

Patterns of Failure

Early failures

Early failures are those resulting from inherent weaknesses present in the as-made condition. For example a multi-core cable which is stripped using wire strippers which have been set too tightly; while stripping the cable some of the conductors are severed and removed. Subsequently, the cable is soldered into position. The joint is tested for continuity and found to be acceptable. However, there now exists a product or system with an inherent weakness which will result in failure in due course. The traditional approach to this is to allow a factor of safety in the design. However, the frontiers of technology have been eating into this indulgence in over- design in order to save weight and increased miniaturisation. Such failures tend to be eliminated during the early life of the product and are

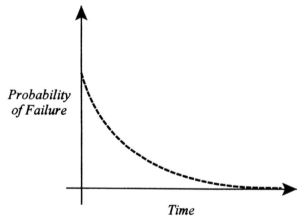

Figure 38

therefore referred to as infant mortalities. In safety critical situations, it has been common practice to use soak tests and/or burn-in techniques to uncover and remove defectives before release.

Random cause failures

The second failure pattern is purely random and refers to those failures which cannot be assigned to any special cause. Continuing with the human analogy, even after infant mortalities have occurred deaths still occur as a result of unpredictable causes such as a strange flu virus or hurricane. Acknowledging that these are unpredictable does not remove man's quest for refining his knowledge of these unknown causes. In such circumstances, it is usual to make contingency plans and use design techniques such as de-rating, redundancy, fail-safe and fail-soft technology (minimising the impact of failure).

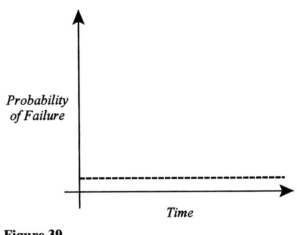

Figure 39

Wear out failures

The third failure process is due to wear out. Components do wear, erode and weaken over a period of time. Fatigue has been the subject of much analysis and other techniques such as Weibull analysis provide information on likely time scales of potential failures.

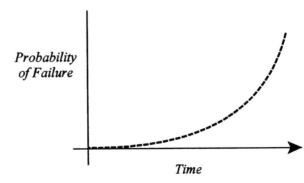

Figure 40

129

Reliability

Combining these failures together produces a failure distribution commonly referred to as the "bathtub curve" for obvious reasons.

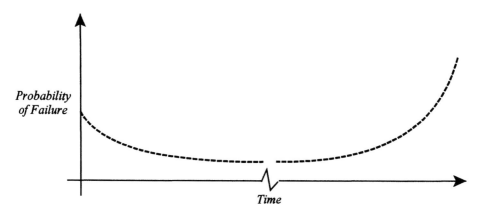

Figure 41

Introduction to Quality Assurance

Conditions in service

It must be remembered that all of the above is dependant on known conditions of use. In many circumstances these may be unknown or unpredictable. This is why it has been necessary to introduce legislation such as the M.O.T. test for vehicles more than three years of age to check safety critical features. Similarly, there is an increasing tendency to design-out do-it-yourself maintenance and servicing of commodities. For example, certain products cannot be bought but only leased so that the producer maintains control over the service and maintenance of his products.

Introduction to Basic Probability Theory

Probabilities are generally related to a scale as follows:

1.0 -   You will die
0.9 -
0.8 -
    First card dealt is not a heart
0.7 -
0.6 -
0.5 -   Tossed coin is heads
0.4 -
0.3 -
    First card dealt is a heart
0.2 -
0.1 -
0 -   You will live forever

Example 1
probability of throwing a 4 with single die   P   =   1/6
                                                     =   0.166

Example 2
probability of cutting a king at cards   P   =   4/52
(4 chances out of 52)   =   0.07692

Reliability

Example 3
probability of a 4 <u>or</u> a 6 with a single die
$$P = 1/6 + 1/6$$
$$= 2/6$$
$$= 0.3333$$

This is called the addition law and applies to OR events:
i.e. if probability of event A is P_A and probability of B is P_B then the probability of A OR B is
$$P_{A \text{ or } B} = P_A + P_B$$

Example 4
probability of a 6 and a 6 with two dice.
All possible combinations may be represented as follows:

1 and 1	2 and 1	3 and 1	4 and 1	5 and 1	6 and 1
1 and 2	2 and 2	3 and 2	4 and 2	5 and 2	6 and 2
1 and 3	2 and 3	3 and 3	4 and 3	5 and 3	6 and 3
1 and 4	2 and 4	3 and 4	4 and 4	5 and 4	6 and 4
1 and 5	2 and 5	3 and 5	4 and 5	5 and 5	6 and 5
1 and 6	2 and 6	3 and 6	4 and 6	5 and 6	6 and 6

From this table it may be seen that there are 36 possible combinations but only one of them is a double six.

Clearly one would not want to create a table every time it is necessary to know how to calculate the probabilities.

Since the probability of the first die is 6 or 1/6 and the probability of the second die is 1/6 their respective probabilities are multiplied to obtain the combined probability thus:

$$P = 1/6 \times 1/6$$
$$1/36$$
$$= 0.0277$$

This is called the multiplication law and applies to AND events!.
i.e. if probability of event A is P_A and probability of B is P_B then the probability of A AND B
is
$$P_{A \text{ and } B} = P_A P_B = P_A \times P_B$$

The addition and multiplication laws can be combined as follows:

Example 5
Probability of 7 with two dice
i.e.   (1 AND 6) OR (2 OR 5) OR (3 AND 4) OR (4 AND 3) OR (5 AND 2) OR (6 & 1)
         $(1/6 \times 1/6) + (1/6 \times 1/6) + (1/6 \times 1/6) + (1/6 \times 1/6) + (1/6 \times 1/6) + (1/6 \times 1/6)$
         = $1/36 + 1/36 + 1/36 + 1/36 + 1/36 + 1/36$
         =   6/36
         =   .1666

This can be applied to a quality application.

Example 6
Consider a batch containing 2% defective and calculate:

   (1) the probability of selecting a defective item.
   (2) the probability of selecting two defective items.
   (3) the probability of a good item followed by a defective.

Probability of one defective P_d = 0.02
Probability of two defectives P_{2d} = $P_d \times P_d$
                                                      = 0.02×0.02 =   0.0004
Probability of a good and a defective $P_{g \; and \; d}$
                                                      = $P_g \times P_d$
                                                      = 0.98×0.02 =   0.0196

Note: If order does not matter i.e. defective followed by good OR defective followed by good

   P   = (0.98×0.02) + (0.02×0.98) i.e. 2×0.0196

Reliability

Example 7

If the chance of failing a batch of goods by sampling is 2%, calculate:

    (1) the chance of failing 5 consecutive batches.
    (2) the chance of passing 5 consecutive batches.
    (3) the chance of failing any two in three.

(1) P_{f5} = 0.02 x   0.02   x   0.02   x   0.02   x   0.02   = 3.2×10^{-9}

        =   0.0000000032

(2) P_{p5} = 0.98^5 =   0.904

(3) P_{FFP} =   0.02   x   0.02   x   0.98   =   0.000392
        P_{FPF} =   0.02   x   0.98   x   0.02   =   0.000392
        P_{PFF} =   0.98   x   0.02   x   0.98   =   <u>0.000392</u>
                                                    0.001176

Systems Reliability

Introduction

When two or more units are linked this is called a system. The links may be in series or parallel or a combination of series and parallel. The reliability of the system depends on the type of link. A series system is an example of AND events in that all units in series must be operable for system success. A parallel system is a an example of OR events in that the system will succeed if one or more units are operable.

Series systems

Consider a system of a given number of units or parts having reliability R1, R2, R3, etc. These may be represented in block form.

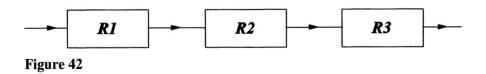

Figure 42

If one component fails, the whole system fails i.e. we have a series situation such as a chain in which if one link fails the whole chain fails. Say R1 = R2 = R3 = 0.9 (probability of success) at a given time. What is the reliability of the system?

Rs   =   R1 x R2 x R3   =   0.9 x 0.9 x 0.9   =   0.73

This is the probability of all devices working at the same time. Analogy is the probability of throwing a dice three times and 1, 2, 3, 4, or 5 coming up each time = 5/6 x 5/6 x 5/6.

Parallel systems

In this situation, if any of the sub-systems operate then the system will work. This is more complex than might at first appear. The simplest approach is to calculate the probability of failure of all sub-systems and subtract from 1. This gives us the probability of success of the system thus:

Probability of all subsystems failing is $P_{1and2and3} = P_1 \times P_2 \times P_3$
Therefore, reliability
$= 1 - ((1-R1) \times (1-R2) \times (1-R3))$

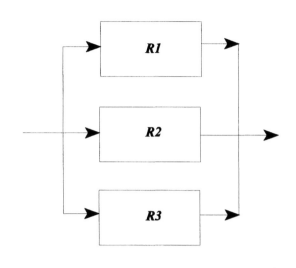

Figure 43

Consider a system of three sub-systems or parts operating in parallel, having reliability R1, R2, R3 respectively. These may be represented in block form as above.

Let us assume that the respective reliabilities are 0.9 each.

$$
\begin{aligned}
Rs \quad &= \quad 1 - ((1 - 0.9) \times (1 - 0.9) \times (1 - 0.9)) \\
&= \quad 1 - (0.1 \times 0.1 \times 0.1) \\
&= \quad 1 - (0.001) \\
&= \quad 0.999
\end{aligned}
$$

This is a very important principle since it explains why cars have dual braking systems or aircraft have triple navigation systems. The provision of parallel systems to improve reliability is called **redundancy**.

PART C

Control of Processes

Control of Supplies

Introduction

A major determinant of quality is the quality of supplies. This refers to anything supplied to the company whether it be material or services. There is sometimes confusion over terminology which needs to be resolved. For example, whenever ISO 9001 refers to the supplier it means the organisation seeking certification. Their suppliers are referred to as sub-contractors. Another term used for sub-contractors is vendors. As far as this section is concerned, the terms supplier and subcontractor will mean the same thing, whether it be for materials or services.

Another term often used in place of purchasing is procurement. This is commonly used in MOD contracts. Procurement is perhaps a more generic name since purchasing implies some payment, whereas procurement may not necessarily involve payment.

However, the important point is that the quality of sub-contracted product (remember product may include services), is under someone else's control and, therefore, presents a vulnerable situation as far as quality assurance is concerned. Organisations such as Marks and Spencer rely totally on their suppliers' quality assurance since they do not make anything themselves. Much can be learned from their methodologies.

Methods of Controlling Suppliers

There is a wide range of approaches and techniques that can be adopted in controlling suppliers.

    i.   Product/process specification
    ii.   Trust
    iii. Sample evaluation
    iv. Receipt inspection
        (1) 100%
        (2) Spot checking
        (3) Percentage sampling
        (4) Statistical sampling
    v.   Second party assessment
        (1) Initial evaluation visit
        (2) Surveillance visits
        (3) Systems audit
    vi. Buyer/seller partnership
    vii. Third party assessment

A number of other factors need to be taken into account before deciding on the most appropriate supplier.

These include:

i. Relative size of purchaser in relation to supplier;
ii. Risk or consequences if the supplied products are not suitable;
iii. Cost of control versus cost of defects.

Product/process specification

In this approach, the product or process is detailed very precisely in a specification. For example, the specification for the printing of cheque books comprises some 50 pages along with templates for checking. All product and/or process parameters are clearly defined in such a way that if they are closely adhered to the product will conform to specification. This is an approach commonly used by Marks and Spencer. When issued to several sub-contractors, the final products will be indistinguishable from each other regardless of where they are made. (See also Product Specification as a basis for Contract and Auditing page 44.)

While there is less excuse for the sub-contractor getting it wrong there is no guarantee that he will always get it right. The sub-contractor would still have to have some means of controlling quality.

Trust

Placing orders on trust means that no checks or other controls are considered necessary. The justification for this approach may be that:

i. It is believed that the sub-contractor has all the necessary arrangements in place to prevent defects.
ii. The consequences of finding something wrong after purchase is not serious or costly.
iii. The purchaser considers that the subcontractor knows more about the product and its fitness for use than they do.

This is a very common approach. Even when purchasers have strict inspection or other controls in place, it is likely that the scope of inspection or controls is restricted to selected features with the remaining features being left to trust. Consider, for example, the purchase of a car. The buyer may go over it with a fine toothcomb checking for obvious damage, together with a test drive prior to acceptance. However, it is highly unlikely that they will inspect anything that is not easily accessible, such as brake pads, for compliance to specification.

The basis of trust may have various foundations:

    a. naive or blind faith,
    b. reputation,
    c. recommendation,
    d. past experience,
    e. third party certification.

Sample evaluation

Prior to placing orders for large quantities, the purchaser may require some evidence that what is to be supplied complies with his requirements. It is not uncommon, therefore, especially with large volume production to require the sub-contractor to supply samples which can be evaluated.

This approach is usually employed in conjunction with other approaches.

Receipt inspection

100% inspection.

This requires some clarification.
One hundred percent inspection may mean inspection of all attributes of a product, or all products, or both.

It is rare to find that it is necessary to inspect all attributes of a product. Some parameters are more significant than others. Some parameters are not readily inspected or can only be inspected by a destructive test. Inspection may introduce its own errors. For example, if it is necessary to dismantle something to inspect it, something may be left out on re-assembly.

Although it may be considered important to perform a dimensional or functional inspection or test at the goods receiving stage the decision to carry out a formal Goods Received Inspection (GRI) requires careful consideration. For example, take a typical company and say they receive 1000 different batches per month, containing an average of 1000 components, each component may have approximately 20 different features that could be checked. If all components were to be checked, then the number of checks would:

Introduction to Quality Assurance

1000 different batches per month * 1000 components per batch * 20 features per component = 20,000,000 features to be checked per month

(This would obviously require a considerable inspection resource)

As a result of the number of checks involved, the organisation may decide:

i.   Not to check every batch or type, but who decides which batch to check-the inspector?
ii. Not to check 100%, i.e. every component. This can be reduced by sampling (BS 6001) but there are a number of risks with sampling.
iii. Not to check all the different features on an item - only the key features but again who decides what a key feature is the inspector?

Say the above gives a 1000% reduction giving 20,000 features per month to be checked, even checking one at a minute each feature will still take approximately two full time inspectors. Is it any wonder that organisations are often complaining that Goods Received Inspection is not cost effective and does not stop poor quality entering the factory?

Another important fact is that 100% inspection does not necessarily mean 100% detection. By way of an example, inspect every letter in the following extract and count the number of times the letter 'e' occurs. Note you may only look at it once. Do not go back or recount. That would be more than 100% inspection.

How many did you find? Ask a friend to do the same and compare your results.

Another important fact is that 100% inspection does not necessarily mean 100% detection. By way of an example, inspect every letter in the following extract and count the number of times the letter 'e' occurs. Note you may only look at it once. Do not go back or recount. That would be more than one hundred percent inspection.

How many did you find? Ask a friend to do the same and compare your results. How can we be sure? 100% inspection is often no better than 90% reliable i.e. it often only detects 90% of the errors. On the other hand some parameters are so critical that they must be independently inspected several times before acceptance. A case in point is the seven-fold checking of every printed banknote prior to release.

How can confidence be placed in the results? One hundred percent inspection is often no better than 90% reliable i.e. it often only detects 90% of the errors. On the other hand some parameters are so critical that they must be independently inspected several times before acceptance. A case in point is the seven-fold checking of every printed banknote prior to release.

Control of Supplies

Spot checks

This approach may be suitable for sub-contractors of known reliability. The checks are usually random and arbitrary. It is based on the same foundation of trust as above.

Percentage sampling

This is a very common approach to inspection usually based on 10% inspection regardless of the batch size. However, it is not commonly known that the approach is fundamentally flawed. A 10% sample of a batch of 5000 items means inspecting 500 items. While 10% of a batch of 50 items means inspecting only five items. The former is a much more stringent test and provides much less risk of accepting a defective batch than the latter. Hence this approach is only consistent with fixed batch sizes.

Statistical sampling using published acceptance plans

There are two fundamental risks when inspecting:

    i.   Accepting a defective batch
   ii.   Rejecting a good batch

These are referred to as the Consumers' Risk and Producers' Risk respectively.

These risks may occur with 100% inspection as well as with sampling inspection. With 100% inspection the risk is based on inspector fatigue. This risk is still present with sampling but is very much reduced owing to the lower volume of inspection. However, when sampling, there is another risk and that is that the sample does not truly represent the batch. The sample may have a smaller percentage of defectives than the batch or vice-versa.

During the Second World War, two statisticians in America, Dodge and Romig, spent many months calculating these risks. They examined the effect of varying the sample size and varying the acceptance criteria. Each combination was called a sample plan. For example, take a batch of 125 items and if there are no more than three defectives accept the batch. This would give a high degree of confidence over a period of time and the average level of defects would be lower than 1%. This is referred to as AQL - Acceptable Quality Level. Another way of stating this is that the AQL is "that lot quality for which the probability of acceptance is .95 (95%)", i.e. AQL = 1% on the operating curve.

Note: this also means that on some occasions the batch quality could be worse than 1% defective and, on others, it could contain more than 1%. The actual risks can be calculated using probability theory and plotted to produce an unique Operating Characteristic Curve (OCC) for a given combination of sample size and accept/reject numbers.

The one shown here is for a sample size of 125 and accept/reject numbers of 3 and 4 respectively.

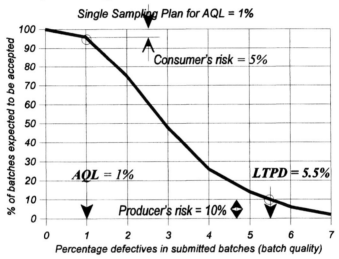

Figure 44

Consumer's Risk and Lot Tolerance Percent Defective

For the sampling plan shown in **Figure 44** , and a consumer's risk defined at 10% , there is a 10% risk that lots containing exactly 5.5% defectives will be accepted. The batch quality (5.5%) corresponding to the consumer's risk is referred to as the Lot Tolerance Percent Defective (LTPD). The consumer's risk is often set at 10%.

Producer's risk and acceptable quality level

For the sampling plan shown in **Figure 44**, and a producer's risk defined at 5% , there is a 5% risk that lots containing exactly 1% defectives will be rejected. The batch quality (1%) corresponding to the producer's risk is referred to as the Acceptable Quality Level (AQL). The producer's risk is often set at 5%.

Acceptance sampling plans

The way these sampling plans work is that items are presented in batches. A representative sample is selected and inspected, and if the sample contains fewer than the reject number then the batch is accepted. If the sample contains a number of defectives equal to or more than the reject number, then the whole batch is rejected. Rejected batches would normally be subjected to 100% inspection to remove the defectives and re-submitted for sampling. This is called an Acceptance Sampling Plan.

An interesting observation from these studies shows that theoretically the batch size does not affect the risks. The risk pattern, the OCC, remains fixed regardless of batch size. In practice, there are other considerations to be taken into account:

i. The fixed sample size means less inspection if items are treated as large batches but a rejected batch means it must be subjected to 100% inspection and consequentially delayed availability of the items for use.

ii. The larger the batch, the more difficult it is to ensure a representative sample.

BS 6001

The British Standards Institute has rationalised the selection of sampling plans from the infinite permutations and provided practical working tables to cover almost any eventuality. These sampling plans are published in BS 6001. BS 6000 provides a definitive guide to the theory, selection and application of sampling plans.

The selection of sampling plans in BS 6001 make use of the preferred number principles covered in a previous unit. They also take into account the cost of inspection and, therefore, identify realistic sample sizes for varying batch sizes. It should be remembered, however, that risks are identical for a given sample size regardless of the batch size and these variations are intended to optimise the total amount of inspection, i.e. the combination of inspecting samples and 100% inspection of rejected batches.

Switching rules

Ideally, an OCC should be as near vertical as possible with 100% probability of accepting all batches better than the AQL and 0% probability of rejecting batches worse than the AQL. This can be achieved to a degree by the use of so called 'switching rules'. Basically, this means that when batches are believed to be better than the AQL, the amount of inspection can be reduced. Conversely, when the quality of batches is believed to be worse than the AQL, the amount of inspection is increased or tightened. This approach can have the effect of combining two OCC's to give a much steeper curve approaching the ideal.

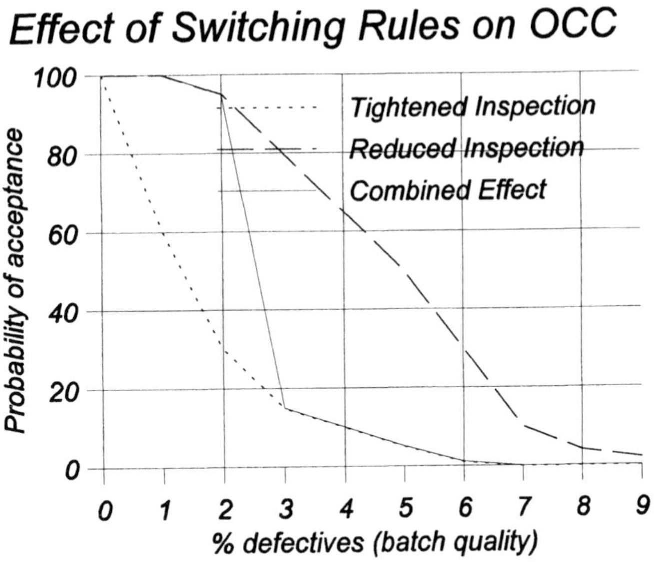

Figure 45

Double, multiple and sequential sampling plans

Another approach towards economising on sampling is to take smaller samples in the first instance. If the batch is either very good or very bad a decision can be made immediately without further sampling. However, if the percentage of defectives is close to the acceptable quality level then further samples may be taken to provide more information. Thus the single sampling plan can be modified to a double sampling plan. This is particularly economic when the quality is consistently good (or bad).

This principle can be extended to multiple sampling plans where up to seven stages of sampling may be needed to make a final decision but with much smaller sample sizes with the prospect of an early decision when quality is very good or very bad.

Indeed this principle can be taken to the extreme where the sample size is one. Samples are inspected until enough information has been gained to make a decision.

Second party evaluation

The previous section presented a defensive approach towards the control of supplies. Many companies, particularly those having a strong purchasing power, prefer to employ a preventive approach.

Second party evaluation means that the purchaser carries out an evaluation of the subcontractor's ability to meet the purchaser's quality standards.

Second party evaluation may be done in varying degrees on a scale as follows:

i.   At a distance by monitoring delivery records and grading subcontractors on some scale.

ii.   By the use of questionnaires to solicit information about the company to enable some evaluation to be made. This is useful for carrying out comparisons between alternative subcontractors.

iii. By visiting the subcontractor's premises to see for themselves how quality is controlled.

iv.   By assessing the subcontractor against some standard. This was the basis of the Ministry of Defence Approved Contractors List (ACL).

v.   By the location of a Quality Assurance Representative at the subcontractor's premises to continuously monitor that contractual requirements, including the quality management systems, are being complied with.

vi.   By regular surveillance visits to verify that quality systems are being maintained.

Surveillance visits vary from full systems audits to simple verification that systems are being maintained by examination of quality system and/or inspection records.

Buyer/Seller partnerships

More and more corporations are now treating their subcontractors as partners in their bid to retain the competitive edge through quality and reliability.

The larger corporations such as Ford Motor Company strike a deal with their subcontractors that they will continue to buy from them on condition that they enter into a continuous improvement programme. The buyers in this case, agree to provide training and development programmes to enable the subcontractor to improve their systems and introduce modern TQM methodologies. Ford Motor Company have been doing this for some time now. Techniques that Ford require subcontractors to implement include Quality Function Deployment, FMECA's, Quality Planning and Statistical Process Control. Japanese companies go further and require the implementation of Quality Circles, Kaizen Quality Improvement Teams and the 5-S's. (See below for a summary of these tools and techniques).

During their surveillance visits the buyers check that there is evidence of these activities being actively applied to all their products or processes.

Third party certification

The major problem with second party evaluation is the prospect of multiple assessment. That is, if a subcontractor has more than one major customer he may be subjected to second party surveillance by each of them. This is not only time consuming but may also create conflicting demands.

It was for this very reason that the British Standards Institute in 1979 published BS 5750 which was later to be adopted by the ISO committee as ISO 9000. In conjunction with this standard, more than 60 certification bodies have been formed and accredited to provide a certificate of assessment to those firms that can demonstrate that they meet the requirements of the standard. Thus by having one certification body the number of visits is restricted to two a year on average. At the same time purchasers can be assured that subcontractors listed in the DTI (Department of Trade and Industry) register of firms of Assessed Capability are managing quality in accordance with an international standard.

This scheme is described in greater detail in an earlier unit.

QS 9000

The car industry has been reluctant to give up their second party involvement with subcontractors. In addition, they considered that the ISO standard did not adequately address the controls considered essential in the manufacture of automotive parts. As a result they have collectively compiled an automotive industry version of ISO 9000 called QS 9000. In addition to the basic requirements of ISO 9000, QS 9000 includes various tools and techniques appropriate to the design and manufacture of automobiles.

Control of Supplies

Thus, Supplier Assurance ranges from the fairly basic approach as described in ISO 9001 (see section on Purchasing) to the very comprehensive approaches, such as the Motor Vehicle Standard QS 9000. Both of these approaches have features that make the approach attractive to buyers; the simple approach may be less demanding in terms of resource but may be considered too vague and not sufficiently product or service specific.

Introduction to Quality Assurance

Elements for consideration when compiling a Purchasing Control procedure

Purchasing procedures should ensure that:

a) Requirements are clearly specified.
b) Supplier performance is known.
c) Any specific quality requirements are specified..

a)   The purchase order:

The Purchase Order should contains all the necessary information for the supplier to satisfactorily fulfil the customer requirements.
The order could contain:

- Name and address of subcontractor from Approved List of Subcontractors
- Identification, description and technical (drawing specification etc.) information.
- Any Inspection and Test criteria (including certification) or Quality Standards to be applied.
- Delivery instructions
- Review of the order (checking and approval of the above).

b)   Assessment of subcontractors:

This could include an audit against the requirements of a recognised Quality Assurance System Standard like ISO 9001 and assessing their ability to meet the customer requirements.

The creation of an Approved List of Subcontractors is usually an internally created list produced as a result of:

- Vendor Rating or from commercially available lists of companies of assessed capability provided by certification bodies or the Department of Trade & Industry.
- Sending questionnaires to existing or prospective subcontractors requesting information about the supplier's Quality Assurance Management System.
- Examination of the supplier's historical performance by the use of such techniques as Vendor Rating.

Vendor Rating: Views on supplier's performance can be very subjective when making a decision on the selection of a subcontractor. As far as possible, supplier performance should be based on objective evidence by one or more of the methods described above. Often, subcontractors are selected on the basis of one person's judgement of a particular supplier's performance. This judgement may be on the basis of price alone. Price alone is not a good basis on which to place an order. Many organisations would be willing, and do pay a price premium for supplies that are to the correct quality and delivered on time. In fact studies have shown that the customer is willing to pay a price premium of up to 30% if the perceived quality standard is higher than the competitors.

There are a number of other factors which may be considered other than price. Although price does need to be included when making a judgement on suppliers' performance. These factors can include:

Price	The rating needs to include price as a factor but because there are various types of subcontractor, e.g. subcontractors of apples and subcontractors of pears comparing the price of apples with the price of pears is not appropriate. Also, the items are often obtained from single source so comparing different subcontractors on the basis of price becomes difficult. One way of overcoming the problem of comparing subcontractors, e.g. subcontractor A's apples with subcontractors B's apples, can be to monitor price increases from the original order price with subsequent orders.
On time Delivery	Number of deliveries on time against the number of late deliveries
Quality	i) Number of batches rejected against the number of orders accepted. (This can include any subsequent problems with deliveries found later).
	ii) Results of any external assessment by giving the subcontractor a rating on a scale from 0 (poor) to 10 (excellent).
Service	Subjective judgement on the subcontractor's ability to react to problems (quality, schedule changes, technical support etc.). This may require discussion with buyers

and engineers to determine the quality of service provided using a rating scale of 0 (poor) to 10 (excellent).

Each of these factors can be given a weighting, for example:

Price   30%
Delivery   20%
Quality   30% (if no audit rating figure)
            15% for rejects + 15% for external audit rating. (The audit rating is a numerical interpretation of the results of an external audit)
Service   20%

Note:
These weightings are not fixed and may be modified for different situations.

The following is an illustration of the way a Vendor Rating Analysis may be carried out to compare two potential suppliers.

Table 17
An example of Vendor Rating Analysis

Factor	Weighting	Formula	Sub-contractor A	Sub-contractor B
Price	30%	$\frac{\text{Original Price}}{\text{Current Price}} * 30\%$	$\frac{10}{12} * 30\% = 25$	$\frac{12}{15} * 30\% = 24$
Delivery	20%	$\frac{\text{On time delivery}}{\text{Total no. of Deliveries}} * 20\%$	$\frac{54}{60} * 20\% = 18$	$\frac{50}{50} * 20\% = 20$
Quality	30%	$\frac{\text{No of batch accepted}}{\text{Total no of batches}} * 15\%$ + Audit Rating * 15%	$\frac{32}{60} * 15$ + $\frac{6}{10} * 15 = 17$	$\frac{45}{50} * 30 = 27$ + (No audit)
Service	20%	Service Rating * 20%	$\frac{5}{10} * 20 = 10$	$\frac{9}{10} * 20 = 18$
Rating	100%		70	89

Control of Supplies

It is important to remember to keep the analysis relatively simple as the Vendor Rating is only a guide to the supplier's performance and does not replace communication, discussion and generally working with the sub-contractor towards the common objective of improving the overall quality performance.

c)   *Goods Receiving Inspection (GRI):*

Almost all organisations perform some form of GRI. It may take the form of a complete inspection and test of the items received against a specification, possibly employing a sampling scheme such as BS 6001. Alternatively, GRI may consist of a check only on quantity, documentation, identification and damage.

Sub-contractor Quality Assurance

Introduction

The following approach towards second party assessment is based on the QS 9000 scheme.

The key elements of a sub-contractor Quality Assurance System could include: planning of quality, process and product quality, system approval, documentation and records.
(See **Figure 46**)

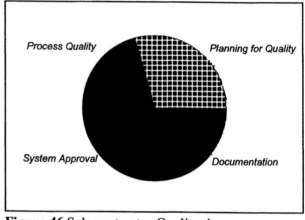

Figure 46 Sub-contractor Quality Assurance

Introduction to Quality Assurance

a)   Planning for quality

The following techniques can be employed to plan for quality, ensuring that before volume supplies or high cost installation is started, all possible sources of poor quality have been considered and addressed.

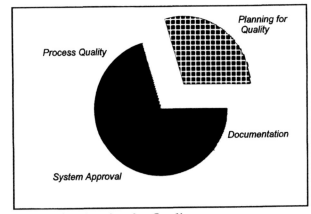

Figure 47 Planning for Quality

Quality Function Deployment: As a project or design progresses, the greater the chance that specific customer's needs and expectations are overlooked or not satisfied. In order not to neglect or overlook 'the voice of the customer', the Quality Function Deployment (QFD) technique has been developed. The aim of QFD is to identify the key customer needs and translate these needs into controls. This control is achieved by establishing what the customer requires and through the various stages of QFD how these requirements will be achieved.

Failure Mode Effects and Criticality Analysis: This technique is used to identify and eliminate possible causes of failure. The technique requires a sequential, disciplined approach by a team to assess systems, products or processes. The technique involves establishing the modes of failure and the effects of failure on the system, product or process. This ensures that all possible failure modes have been fully identified and ranked in order of their importance. (See section FMECA).

Quality Control Planning: Once the QFD and FMECA are completed an excellent understanding of the customer needs and expectations will have been gained. Any potential system or product failures will also have been identified. Consequently, the process or project can be properly planned.

The stages involved are:

i.   Defining the process. This can often be established by drawing a flow diagram of the process showing each of the key process stages and the sequence.
ii.   Identifying the parameters or key stages that require control.
iii.   Specifying the criteria for judging conformity.

iv.   Deciding on the means of control.
v.   Deciding on the means of assessment.
vi.   Preparing the appropriate documentation
vii.   Monitoring the effectiveness of the plan.

Process capability studies: All processes are subject to variation. This variation may be small and insignificant or alternatively the variation could be excessive allowing products to be manufactured outside the specification. It is, therefore, important to understand the extent to which a process will vary before starting manufacture, thereby avoiding costly scrap or start/stop manufacture.

One method of determining the ability of a process to meet specification is by conducting a Process Capability Study. This is where the process is statistically evaluated to determine the process ability to conform to specification.

b)   Process and Product Quality

Statistical Quality Control (SQC): Having determined the ability of the process to meet specification, controls need to be applied which continually monitor the process for quality and make continuous improvements. This involves taking regular measurements of process variation and comparing these observations with pre-

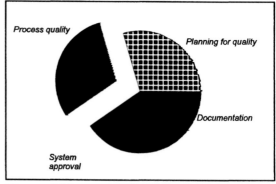

Figure 48 Process & Product Quality

determined control limits of variation. This comparison can best be accomplished graphically on control charts. The application of SQC gives the opportunity to implement operator quality control, assisting in reinforcing the operator's responsibility for the quality of his own work and gives a sense of pride in his work.

Introduction to Quality Assurance

c)   System and product approval

Assessment, review and evaluation: When a product specific Quality Control Plan has been established, then an audit can be performed to confirm compliance with the agreed Quality Plan including the application of SQC. The results of the assessment can then be reviewed and evaluated to identify any areas for possible improvement.

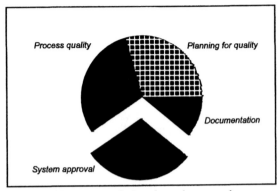

Figure 49 System & Product Approval

Initial Sample approval: Provide statistical data in the form of Process Capability Study results to confirm the ability to manufacture all product features to the specified requirements.

d)   Documentation and records

Procedures: When the above stages have been completed, then procedures need to be documented that describe the tasks to be performed together with any specific work instructions that may be necessary. These procedures may be subject to change. In the event of changes being necessary, change control procedures need to be agreed to ensure that documentation is circulated to the relevant departments and that the documentation is kept up-to-date.

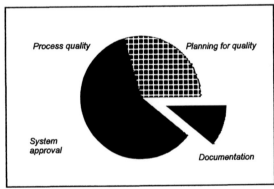

Figure 50 Documentation and Records

Records: Various records will need to be maintained providing documentary evidence of the satisfactorily completion of the above stages, e.g.. QFD and FMECA. Records of the inspection and testing performed will also need to be maintained possibly in the form of SQC or Process Capability Study results.

Process Control

Quality Control Strategy

Introduction

It can be seen from previous chapters that the modern approach towards Quality Assurance is the preventive approach. This involves anticipating and preparing for a right first time result.

Step 1 Start right

▸ Check that the operator, machine, tools etc. are capable with respect to the specified tolerance.
▸ Check instructions, drawings and documentation are available and at the right issue.
  Set up the machine.
▸ Inspect the first off.
▸ If the first off is not within tolerance readjust the machine and repeat until correct.

Step 2 Keep right

▸ Inspect samples at suitable intervals.
▸ Plot inspection results on control charts.
▸ Interpret control chart and take corrective action when necessary.

Step 3 Finish right

▸ Inspect the last item and plot on the chart.
▸ Complete records and return documentation.
▸ Protect components for transport to the next stage.
▸ Return tools for refurbishment and safe storage.
▸ Carry out any planned maintenance.

The benefits of this approach are:.
▸ Manufacture of defective items is avoided.
▸ Defective work is prevented and, therefore, does not result in field failures.
▸ Increased manufacturing efficiency and profitability.

> **Modern Techniques = PREVENTION of out-of limit parts**
> **= Savings/Benefits**

It is clearly more sensible to avoid waste and hold-ups by adopting a policy of **PREVENTION** and **"Right First Time"**.

Development and identification of the quality control strategy

This section discusses the Quality Control issues associated with various processes and attempts to develop a suitable Quality Control Strategy for each process type. Below are listed some possible scenarios that may require a Quality Control Strategy to be developed:

a. A Batch Process - Where items of a similar type are collected into packets or batches of work for processing through the various process stages. For example, batches of say 20 components travelling round the various stages in a machine shop; batches of orders to process through the sales and then invoicing departments; batches of students to be processed through their various course stages and lectures.

b. A Flow Process - A continuous process of manufacture. For example; an oil refinery, food or paint production,

c. An Assembly Process - The assembly of an item from various sub-assemblies or parts. For example; car, computer, a piece of capital equipment. Here it is important to draw a distinction between Mass Production Assembly (a motor vehicle) and one off assemblies (an oil rig).

d. A Service Process - The provision of assistance or aid. For example; bank, hospital, hotel, repair and maintenance, software support, etc..

e. A Design Process - The process of researching, developing and designing a product or service. For example; design of a motor vehicle, an oil rig, a training course.

Each of the above process types could require the development of a different Quality Control Strategy. There are many models that can be used for the purpose of this. ISO 90001 or ISO 9004 could be used as a general model; Guide to Good Laboratory or Manufacturing Practice for the medical or food industry; QS 9000 for the mass production and assembly processes and Boeing's DL 9000 for the Aerospace or capital equipment process. Following is a simple approach. Namely, start right, keep right and finish right[11]. Now this model may be too simplistic when applied to very large organisations or processes but it has proved to be a very useful tool in circumstances where there is no directly applicable model available or when examining short or small businesses processes. In manufacturing industries the idea of start right, keep right and finish right or in manufacturing terms may be seen as first-off, patrol and last-off inspection. Obviously having determined the Quality Control strategy, then Inspection Planning (see page 217) has a role to play in finalising the overall approach.

Batch process - *Start Right*. This entails ensuring that all the correct documentation, equipment, material and people are established before the process is run. The correct documentation includes the process method, instructions and specification (target values and tolerances) and inspection schedule; the tooling and equipment is of an adequate standard (see section on process capability studies); that the raw materials to be processed are from a qualified source (see Section on purchase control); that the personnel running the process are adequately trained and qualified.

One way of showing that personnel are adequately trained is by the use of a Training Matrix which shows the training status of the personnel. These matrices can also be reviewed by supervision during any training appraisal and when appropriate further or new training is given to the staff.

---

[11]   See "R.H.Caplen - A Practical Approach to Quality Control"

Introduction to Quality Assurance

Records of training may be shown on a training matrix, an example of which is shown below:

Process Name	Filling			
Process Owner	J Smith			
Person Name Stars	Person A ∗∗∗	Person B ∗	Person C ∗∗∗∗	Person N ∗∗∗∗∗
Task Name				
Task 1	A	B	C	D
Task 2	D	C	B	A
Task 3	A	A	A	A
Task n	B	B	B	B

Five Star Training. These are the levels for each process. There would be another set of Training Matrices for other processes.

The stars associated with each person are process based and indicate:

∗∗∗∗∗   Able to teach the process; self inspect; set up; complete the process without supervision.

∗∗∗∗   Able to complete the process; self inspect; set up with supervisor check off.

∗∗∗   Limited experience, can complete the process but with supervision check off.

∗∗   Very limited or no experience, can complete the process but with supervision..

∗   Received induction understands health and safety.

The letters are task based and are associated with person and task. These letters indicate;

A   *Able to teach the process; self inspect; set up; complete the process without supervision.*

B   *Able to complete the process; self inspect; set up with supervisor check off.*

C   *Limited experience, can complete the process but with supervision check off.*

D   *Very limited or no experience, can complete the process but with supervision.*

E   *Received induction understands health and safety.*

Process Control

Before the process run, first - off- inspection may be required. Note, first - off -inspection does not necessarily mean it has to be performed by an inspector (more often this will be an operator). The role of the inspector may be to complete an audit of the first off process. Once the first off has satisfactorily passed inspection the route card will probably be up-dated for inspection status purposes.

Table 17 1st - off Inspection Audit Check List

Process Name:		
Batch No:		
#	Check	Result
1	Is the quality standard adequately defined?	
2	Is the quality standard achievable?	
3	Is all documentation (process, inspection, routing, etc.) available?	
4	Are correct gauges, tools and equipment available?	
5	Has the operator been trained?	
6	Are the process controls set correctly?	

Batch process - *Keep Right*. This should be the inspection schedule in action. Note again inspection does not necessarily mean it has to be performed by an inspector (more often this will be an operator). The inspection schedule may detail for each process stage:

- The features to be checked (together with target and tolerances)
- The inspection equipment to be used

Table 18 Patrol Inspection Audit Check List

Process Name:		
Batch No		
#	Check	Result
1	Are the operator checks being performed correctly?	
2	Are the records being maintained?	
3	Is corrective action being taken when required?	
4	Is the work adequately segregated and identified?	

160

Introduction to Quality Assurance

- The frequency of inspection and
- The recording method (see Section on Control Charts)

The Inspector's role may be to audit that the operator checks are being performed correctly and recorded. See Table - Patrol Inspection Audit Check List.

Batch process - *Finish Right*. This stage could consist of completion of a last-off which may be a 100% or sample check of the completed batch items. However, this check should be unnecessary if the operator checks have been performed correctly.

Table 19 Last - off Inspection Audit Check List

Process Name:		
Batch No		
#	Check	Result
1	Have the final checks been correctly performed?	
2	Have all the records been completed?	
3	Has all the work been correctly identified and any rejects adequately segregated?	
4	If rejects have been made, has the appropriate corrective action been identified?	
5	Is the product adequately protected?	
6	Are all the gauges, tooling, equipment in a satisfactory condition?	

Process Control

Flow process - *Start Right*. With a continuous process one of the key issues is that it is possible to make a considerable amount of product before a problem is discovered. For example, an oil refinery or a company making soup. It is, therefore, essential that the start right and keep right principles are adhered to, as finish right will only indicate, that there is a major problem. (It may, however, be of some comfort to know, fortunately this is one problem which hopefully, will not reach the customer.)

Activities associated with applying starting right to flow processes could be quality planning and a detailed check of the process set up. Environmental issues may also be worthy of consideration. With specific reference to food production, cleanliness and hygiene for people, equipment and buildings will need to have been addressed. Issues such as pest control, building and equipment maintenance, and reliability become of paramount importance.

Flow process - *Keep Right*. Generally this will consist of monitoring checks of the process output by the laboratory, equipment process setting and parameter monitoring, either remotely or by the machine operator.

Flow process - *Finish Right*. See Flow Process Keep Right

Assembly process - *Start Right*. One of the key issues associated with Quality Control of the assembly process is that it is often not possible to know if the assembly will work until tested and, even then, reliability of the assembly cannot always be guaranteed until used by the customer. These two issues again indicate the importance of starting and keeping right rather than just finishing right. However the final test is of importance to avoid installation, commissioning and warranty problems.

In the mass production industry, great effort is place on Starting Right. Control of supplied material is essential if the assembly process is going to continue to work efficiently and effectively. (See the section Sub-contractor Quality Assurance 152)

Assembly process - *Keep Right*. Consideration also needs to be given to the economics of the assembly tools with specific reference to fool proofing or Poka-yoke[12].

---

[12] *Poka-yoke*   Shigeo Shingo "Poka-yoke"

Introduction to Quality Assurance

In Japan it was found that the use of the term fool proofing was offensive so it was changed to *poka* (inadvertent errors) *yokeru* (to avoid) as an approach to avoiding errors. There are a number of different types of errors just as there are a number of different types of defects, See page 206 Inspection Errors. It is important to understand the distinction between these differing types of errors and defects to determine the approach to eliminating or avoiding them. Eliminating the errors can involve a fool proof method, avoiding errors may require a specific inspection approach.

With Poka-yoke there are a number of approaches to avoiding errors. For example some methods of avoiding human errors could be:

- Location pins which only allow the assembly to be built in the correct orientation.
- Visual or audible alarms when items are misplaced or incorrectly positioned.
- Limit switches which stop machine operation if components are not correctly positioned.
- Stops or counters which clearly identify an incorrect attribute eg weight or size
- Check lists to aid or remind operators. (Would you want to fly on a plane in which the pilot has not completed their pre-flight check list?)

The process of completing a poka-yoke exercise would be to:

a. Build quality into the process from the start.
b. Build a team to:
    i. Identify the sources of defects.
    ii. Identify the sources of error.
    iii. Determine a suitable solution.
    iv. Implement and test the solution.

Assembly process - *Finish Right*. Final testing of the product to ensure that the product in all respects complies with the customer and legal requirements. The final test specification and instruction needs to focus on the functional aspects of the product rather than any individual features of each assembly.

Process Control

The test specification could include:

a. A statement of requirements for the Finished Product covering

    i. Equipment (Visual)
- Mechanical
- Electrical

    etc

    ii. Equipment (Functional)
- Free cycling (not producing)
- Simulating actual condition of use
- Actual condition of use
- Health and safety
- External standards

b. The type of control chart to be used to record the results of the test could include:

    i. The test to be performed, see above list.

    ii. The target and tolerances to be achieved.

    iii. The frequency with which the measurement should be taken, i.e. if the test is of a piece of capital equipment, how frequently should the equipment performance be measured? Measuring this capital equipment performance also provides an opportunity to determine the reliability of the equipment i.e how often does the fitter need to adjust or repair the equipment, to maintain its performance?

    iv. The sample size that needs to be taken.

    v. The duration of the test - as suggested above this needs to be of a duration that will provide adequate levels of confidence in the reliability of the equipment.

    vi. If control charts are to be employed then the recording method will need to be established (attribute or variable charts).

Service process - *Start Right,* In service organisations this usually means determining and specifying the customers' requirements. Not having a clear understanding of the customers' requirement is one the most significant causes of quality failure. In a hospital or bank a clear understanding of customer requirements may be stated in their mission statement or quality goal.

If one takes a motor vehicle garage which maintains and repairs motor vehicles as an example of a service process, then their control of Starting Right may consist of statement regarding the range of vehicles they are capable of maintaining and a booking procedure that clearly identifies the customer needs.

Other aspects that will require controlling at this stage will include a service manual, garage equipment and personnel in terms of their training .

Service process - *Keep Right.* In the example used of a garage, the technicians will be following the manufacturers' recommendations regarding the repair, maintenance and testing of the vehicles. Their training and experience should also ensure that the correct inspections are performed.

These checks performed by the technicians could be augmented by regular supervisor audits. These audits would confirm the quality of the work and that the technician is observing the prescribed procedures.

One of the techniques employed by service industries to maintain the appropriate standards is the 5S approach.

Introduction: The 5S is a systematic approach to establishing and maintaining housekeeping standards. With this method, divisions or departments within organisations adopt and implement their own housekeeping programme, used as a means of improving quality, safety and productivity.

The Programme: This programme is based on the Japanese 5S Housekeeping programme[13] which has been successfully adopted in a number of organisations. Although originally the programme was mainly applied to manufacturing organisations, the programme has relevance to service organisations as well. Below is an interpretation of the 5S programme for a service organisation. The 5S's referred to are based on the Japanese words:

---

[13]   Samuel K Ho - TQM An Integrated Approach

Process Control

- Seiri or Sorting (clearing out or arranging).
- Seiton or Simplifying (configuring or tidying).
- Seiso or Sweeping (cleaning).
- Seiketsu or Standardising (clean condition or cleanliness).
- Shitsuke or Self Discipline (culture, training or breeding).

The benefits in an office environment are that this approach has the potential to reduce the number of ledgers, forms and documents. It can improve file retrieval and archiving times. Possibly and most importantly, it provides a catalyst for team building and office process improvement. Offices often provide the customer with their first impression of the organisation and this may reflect (in the customer's view), our approach to work.

The overall aim is to encourage a *"one is best"* campaign of the office: one item of equipment, one file and one filing system, one-page memos, one-hour meetings, one -minute telephone calls, one-day processing,

Seiri or sorting (Clearing out or arrangements)

This refers to clearing out anything and everything that is not required in the workplace. Photographs (coloured with photograph dates) can be taken of the workplace before starting the clearing out process. This is to bench mark or identify the current status in order to show what improvements have been made. A tagging system can be used by the personnel responsible for the area to identify any items or documents not directly involved with their work place or surrounding area.

Seiton or simplifying (Configuring or tidying)

The tasks or activity area needs to be organised or configured in order to ensure that items are located correctly and can be easily found. Every desk and storage area could have its own address. In this way the whole area can then be organised into an address grid. The various work areas, desks, copying, stores, cabinets, etc. could be (colour) coded .

Seiso or sweeping (Cleaning)

The purpose of cleaning is to maintain the workplace in a suitable condition for the activities and tasks that need to be performed. This is achieved by ensuring that all excess material or documentation is suitably located or disposed of. All areas that have to be cleaned should be clearly identified with responsibilities allocated and frequency pre-determined.

Seiketsu or standardising (Clean condition or cleanliness)

The work area needs to be maintained in a clean and tidy condition at all times, with no accumulation of unnecessary items or documentation.

Shitsuke or self discipline (Culture, training or breeding)

A working environment needs to be created that welcomes constructive criticism and an improvement culture. This environment is essential if problem points are to be quickly and easily identified and rectified. All work areas need to be clean and tidy, and free of unnecessary materials and product. Only machines, tools, instruments and equipment which are actually used shall be in place. There should be techniques for removing unnecessary items. Work areas should be organised and all machines/equipment labelled and easily identified. All stored and necessary items should be immediately visible. Maximum and minimum stock levels of consumables needs to be clearly visible. All work areas and passage ways should be clearly separated. The storage location of tools/instruments should be clearly labelled for ease of operation and return. The work place should be free of dirt, spills, clothing, and other extraneous materials. All machines, tools, equipment and containers should be clean and in good condition. Responsibilities for cleaning and the state of items should be allocated and cleaning should be a regular part of work. The work place should be standardised and there should be a system for regular clearing up, organising and cleaning. There should be training and discipline in housekeeping. All staff should be aware of procedures and all procedures strictly followed. All housekeeping actions should be taken promptly and all actions and controls should be effective. Audits should be conducted against housekeeping procedures.

All Shitsuke should be practised until it has become natural habit.

Detailed below is a check list which could be employed when conducting a 5S assessment.

Process Control

5S Check List			Section:	Checker:				
Marks: . . . . %			Previous Marks: . . . . %	Date:				
5S	#	Checking Item	Evaluation Criteria	0	1	2	3	4
Clearing Up (20 Marks)	1	Task inputs & Deliverables	No unnecessary paper work or finished documentation left lying around.					
	2	Equipment (utilisation)	All equipment is in regular use.					
	3	Equipment (condition)	All equipment is regularly serviced & maintained.					
	4	Visual control	There are no unnecessary items left lying around on tops of desks, cabinets or chairs.					
	5	Standards for disposal	Items and documentation are properly disposed of, e.g. tag items.					

Introduction to Quality Assurance

5S	#	Checking Item	Evaluation Criteria	0	1	2	3	4
Organising (20 Marks)	1	Equipment labelling	Equipment is clearly labelled.					
	2	Necessary items	All necessary items can be quickly identified and located.					
	3	Consumables	Minimum and maximum stock levels are established and visible.					
	4	Dividing lines	Work areas and passageways are clearly divided.					
	5	Equipment and tools	Storage locations of tools and equipment are clearly marked of ease of use and return.					
Cleaning (20 marks)	1	Floors	Clean and clear					
	2	Equipment	Tidy and serviceable					
	3	Desks and cabinets	Clear and tidy					
	4	Computers and ancillaries	Tidy and serviceable					
	5	Health and safety	Fire, protective equipment, lifting & handling, COSHH, disaster recovery.					
Standardising (20 Marks)	1	One method of working, e.g. one day processing	Process based procedures available Targets set and records kept of processing performance.					
	2	One set of files, e.g. one location, one copy, one minute file storage and retrieval	Examine file condition Test ability to store and retrieve records in one minute.					

Process Control

5S	#	Checking Item	Evaluation Criteria	0	1	2	3	4
	3	One set of documentation e.g. forms and one-page memos	Examine forms Examine memos					
	4	One piece of equipment	Examine equipment availability and quantity					
	5	One-minute telephone calls, one-hour meetings,	Review telephone call practice and duration Review meeting times.					
Training & Discipline (20 Marks)	1	5S Programme and audit results	Result published, reviewed and improvements made.					
	2	Team building	Process improvement. Meetings held and real solutions identified.					
	3	Team briefing and communication	Team briefing held.					
	4	Absenteeism and employee turn over	Review records.					
	5	Recognition	Recognition for achievement is observed.					
Total								

Key

Scores	
0	Very Poor
1	Poor
2	Average
3	Good
4	Very Good

Introduction to Quality Assurance

These audit check lists could be reviewed and analysed at a pre-determined frequency to show the improvements made.

Service Process - *Finish Right*. To return to the example of the motor vehicle garage, once all the maintenance and repairs have been completed and before the work sheet is signed off, the vehicle would need to be road tested. This confirms that the vehicle has been safely repaired and that there are no other unreported faults.

The use of a reply card could possibly be left for the business to gauge customer reaction to the quality of the service provided.

Process Control

Design process - *Start Right*. The design or project control process. (See Section on Design Control). Initially it is important to have established project and design procedures and codes of practice, so that a clear statement of working practices is defined. These procedures need to address the establishment of the customer's requirements including issues such as document control, specification assurance, document validation and verification methods and project sizing. Once the project has been established then the project risks can be established by the use of risk analysis techniques such as: Failure Mode Effect and Criticality Analysis, Fault Tree Analysis, etc. With the potential risk understood, project and quality planning can be completed. The risk analysis should provide information regarding the potential risk to the project and the quality plan should deal with, amongst other things, the way in which these risks will be addressed, minimised or eliminated. The quality plan could also include the timing of the project audits.

Design process - *Keep Right*. With the project under way project records should be established and created. These will need to include records of configuration management. Part of keeping the project or design right can be approvals of documentation, e.g. drawings and calculation, reviews and monitoring (e.g. cost, specification, time and health and safety). The results of any project audits should also be available for corrective action and closed down.

Design process - *Finish Right*. At the conclusion of the design or project, a validation of project deliverables should be completed. This will ensure that the project complies with and addresses customer requirements.

The Changing Role of Inspectors, Operators and Setters

Traditionally the purpose of inspection was to filter out defective work from being further processed or reaching the customer. Work which can be salvaged is returned up the line for re-working. With the new approach, the purpose of inspection is to collect information about the process as part of an information system and, instead of defective work being fed back, information is relayed to operators and setters so that the process controls can be adjusted to prevent future defectives being made.

In many circumstances, since inspection is being done 'on the job', periodically it is feasible and sensible that the inspection and recording of inspection results are done by the operator.

Process Variability

No matter what precautions are taken, no two items are absolutely identical. Differences may be barely measurable but they exist and that is why tolerances are allowed on drawings and specifications.

A manufacturing process, no matter how precise, is subject to a very large number of random disturbances, each so small as to be individually insignificant but which in combination, cause the results of the process to deviate slightly from the objective.

The inherent variability thus caused is a characteristic of the process. It is the basic variability which is always present when that particular process is in operation and is called the RESIDUAL variability.

The causes of variation can be divided into machine and process variations.

Machine variations

Machine variations are purely and simply those variations attributable to the machine only. It is the best that a machine can be expected to produce given ideal conditions. Machines vary in their capabilities owing to their age and condition or the tolerances to which the machine was constructed. For a given machine some functions may be more capable than others. For example, a drilling machine will generally be more precise (have a better capability) on hole diameter than on position. Some examples of the relative capabilities of common manufacturing processes are shown below.

Typical Process Capabilities

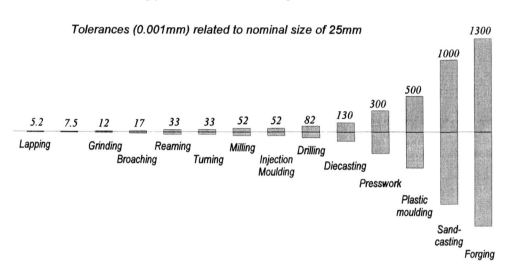

Tolerances (0.001mm) related to nominal size of 25mm

Process variations

Process variations are those over and above the machine variations which are attributable to circumstances around the machine. They include the effect of environmental fluctuations such as temperature and humidity, variations in raw materials, variations in operator attention, variations from shift to shift and so on.

The first important check, therefore, is to consider whether the machine and subsequently the process are both capable of doing the job to the specification. This will require machine and process capability studies to be carried out.

The sources of variation can be further categorised into two types:

i)   Common causes, otherwise known as random causes, and
ii)   Special causes, otherwise known as non-random or assignable causes.

Introduction to Quality Assurance

i) Common causes

Common causes appear to follow a random pattern and are due to inherent variations in the machine or process. For a particular machine or process, the pattern of variation will be characterised by its location, spread, and shape. The combination of these characteristics is called the machine capability in the case of the machine and the process capability in the case of the process. It is the natural tolerance of a stable machine or process.

In general, improvements in machine and process capabilities having only common cause variations, can only be achieved through detailed analysis to identify and isolate particular causes. This usually requires managerial action such as overhauling or replacing a machine, changing to more reliable supplies of materials, providing better tooling, providing further training for operators and so on.

ii) Special causes

Variations due to special causes do not form a random pattern but quite definitely indicate a shift, trend, cycle or otherwise systematic variation such as peaks or troughs. For a stable process, two thirds of the measurements should lie within the middle third of the capability band with the other third being equally divided into the outer two thirds. In addition, no more than seven points in a row should be consistently above the mean, below the mean or progressively up or down.

In general, variations due to special causes can be controlled by local actions such as resetting the machine controls, taking a lighter cut, providing more immediate feedback of performance to the operator etc.

Process capability studies

Before allocating a job to a given machine or process, it is necessary to establish whether the process is capable of meeting the specification. A simple approach is described below:

a)   Set the process to meet its target figure. This would normally be its mid point of specification.

b)   Ensure the process is stable and under control.

c)   Take 50 consecutive units from the process and measure them accurately to one more decimal place than the specified tolerance, e.g. if the specified tolerance is ±0.01mm, then measure to the nearest .001mm.

d)   Assuming that the distribution of results forms a smooth bell shaped curve (approximating a normal distribution), calculate the arithmetical mean $\bar{x}$ and the standard deviation σ of the 50 units.

e)   The process capability is considered to be six standard deviations (6σ). Now compare the six standard deviations with the specified tolerance thus:

$$Cp = \frac{specified\ tolerance}{6\sigma}$$

The potential process capability

The potential process capability is the best that the process can achieve having eliminated special cause variations. The process is said to be stable when the variations are due to random causes only. Six standard deviations are considered to contain 99.7% of all items made. To determine if a process is capable the statistic Cp needs to be calculated,

If Cp = 1 then approximately 3 in every 1,000 will be outside the specification.

This means that values of Cp greater than 1, say 1.5 or even 2.0, are desirable. Diagrammatically this may look like this:

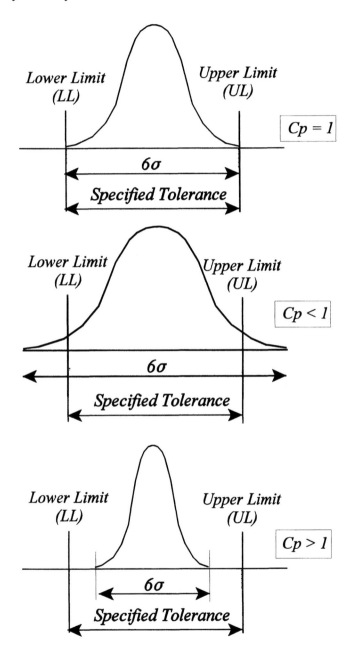

Figure 52

Process Capability Studies

Example

The diameter of a sample of 40 bolts was measured with the following results:

7.31	7.47	7.55	7.2	7.45
7.49	7.62	7.86	7.44	7.39
7.38	7.57	7.63	7.24	7.76
7.55	7.56	7.18	7	7.83
7.57	7.24	7.32	7.39	7.42
7.35	7.63	7.41	7.4	7.3
7.48	7.49	7.27	7.51	7.51
7.73	7.12	7.37	7.48	7.14

Plotting these chronologically

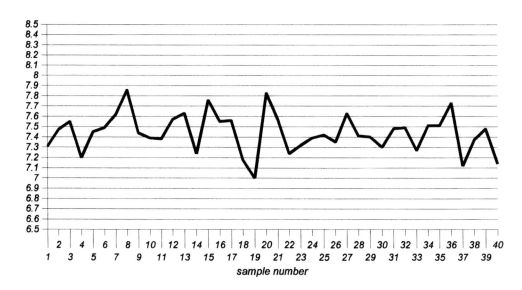

Figure 53

178

Class limits	Nominal value N_i	Tally	Freq. X_i
7.80-7.89	7.845	11	2
7.70-7.79	7.745	11	2
7.60-7.69	7.645	111	3
7.50-7.59	7.545	~~1111~~ 11	7
7.40-7.49	7.445	~~1111~~ ~~1111~~	10
7.30-7.39	7.345	~~1111~~ 111	8
7.20-7.29	7.245	1111	4
7.10-7.19	7.145	111	3
7.00-7.09	7.045	1	1

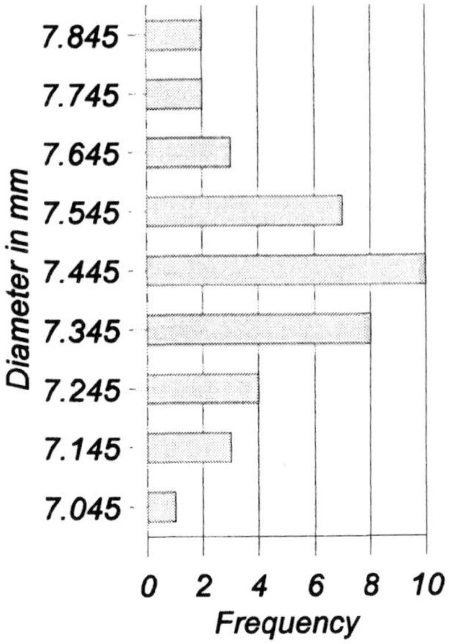

Figure 54

These values need to be grouped into approximately 10 intervals to create a frequency diagram. Using a calculator with a mean and standard deviation (σ) facility, calculate the mean and standard deviation thus:

$$Mean\ \bar{x} = \frac{\sum_{i=1}^{9} x}{n} = N_i X_i$$

$$\bar{x} = 7.440$$

$$Standard\ deviation\ \sigma = \sqrt{\frac{\sum_{i=1}^{9} (\bar{x} - x_i)^2}{n}}$$

$$\sigma = 0.1899$$

Process Capability = 6σ = 1.139

Process Capability Studies

In other words the process is currently producing components in the range:
$$\bar{x} \pm 3\sigma$$
$$= 6.8703 \text{ to } 8.0097$$

Now suppose that the specified tolerance was, say, $7.5 \pm .5$ then clearly, the process is not capable of producing 100% non-defectives. For one thing, the mean is offset from the nominal and secondly, the spread is wider than the specified tolerance.

Process Capability Index

A Cpk value, called the process capability index, may also be helpful as this takes into account the *accuracy*, i.e. the location of the mean, of the process.

$$Cpk = \frac{UL - \bar{x}}{3\sigma} \quad or \quad \frac{\bar{x} - LL}{3\sigma}$$

whichever is the smaller. As with the Cp, the Cpk must be greater than 1 to avoid defectives being produced.

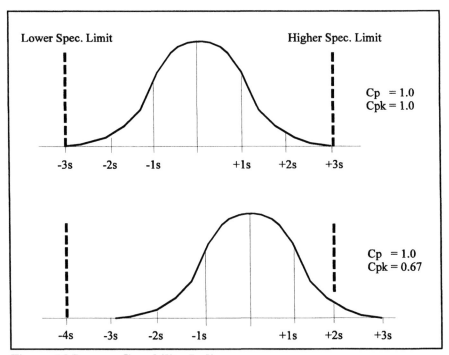

Figure 55 Process Capability Indices

At this stage, a basic knowledge of capability will suffice. Some examples follow. Long term movement and variation of the process is possible and further control of processes will be discussed later.

Example 1

$$\text{Specification} \quad = \quad 1000 \pm 50$$
$$\sigma \quad = \quad 20 \text{ units}$$

Assuming a stable process, which has been adjusted to be central between the specified limits, calculate the Cp and Cpk.

$$\text{Tolerance} \quad = \quad 100 \text{ units}$$

$$\text{Cp} \quad = \quad \frac{100}{6 \times 20} \quad = \quad 0.83$$

Process capability (Cpk)

$$\text{Cpk} \quad = \quad \frac{\text{upper limit - mean}}{3\sigma} \quad \text{or} \quad \frac{\text{mean - lower limit}}{3\sigma}$$

whichever is the smaller.

$$\text{Cpk} \quad = \quad \frac{50}{3 \times 20} \quad = \quad 0.83$$

Note, since the process is assumed to be central, Cpk will be equal to Cp, i.e. .83

Process Capability Studies

Example 2.

Specification = 115±5

σ = 1 unit, x̄ = 112 units

Calculate Cp and Cpk.

$$Cp = \frac{10}{6 \times 1} = 1.67$$

$$Cpk = \frac{112 - 110}{3 \times 1} = 0.67$$

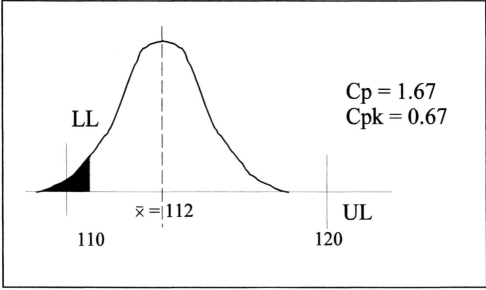

Figure 56

Example 3

UL = 50 units, LL = 45 units
σ = 0.2 units, x̄ = 48.5 units
Calculate Cp and Cpk.

$$Cp = \frac{5}{6 \times 0.2} = 4.17$$

$$Cpk = \frac{50 - 48.5}{3 \times 0.2} = 2.5$$

Process capability studies exercises

Calculate the Cp and Cpk values and draw the likely distribution curves from the data provided.

Example or Data Set No.	Target Value	Tolerance	Average $\bar{x}$	Standard Deviation σ
1	6	±6	6	2
2	5	±5	7	1.67
3	3	±3	3	3

1st Data Set

$$Cp = \frac{\text{Total Tolerance}}{6\sigma}$$

$$Cp = \frac{12}{6*2}$$

$$Cp = 1$$

The process is capable

$$Cpk = \text{The minimum of}$$

$$= \frac{\text{Upper Tolerance} - \bar{x}}{3\sigma}$$

$$\text{or} \quad \frac{\bar{x} - \text{Lower Tolerance}}{3\sigma}$$

$$Cpk = \frac{12-6}{3*2} = 1$$

The process is set correctly

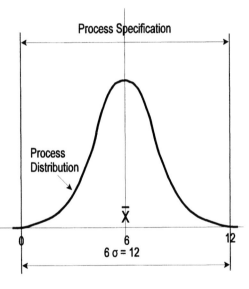

Process Specification

Process Distribution

$\bar{X}$

6

6 σ = 12

0   12

Figure 57 Interpretation of PCS results

183

2nd Data Set

$$Cp = \frac{\text{Total Tolerance}}{6\sigma}$$

$$Cp = \frac{10}{6 * 1.67}$$

$$Cp = 1$$

The process is capable

$$Cpk = \text{The minimum of}$$

$$= \frac{\text{Upper Tolerance} - \bar{x}}{3\sigma}$$

$$\text{or} \quad \frac{\bar{x} - \text{Lower Tolerance}}{3\sigma}$$

$$Cpk = \frac{18 - 14}{3 * 1} = 0.667$$

The process is not set correctly

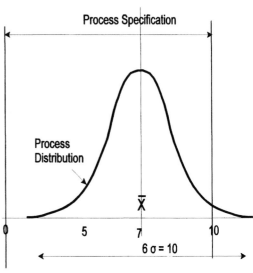

Figure 58 Interpretation of PCS results

3rd Data Set

$$Cp = \frac{\text{Total Tolerance}}{6\sigma}$$

$$Cp = \frac{6}{6*3}$$

$$Cp = 0.333$$

The process is not capable

$Cpk = $ The minimum of

$$= \frac{\text{Upper Tolerance } - \ \bar{x}}{3\sigma}$$

or $\dfrac{\bar{x} \ - \text{ Lower Tolerance}}{3\sigma}$

$$Cpk = \frac{6-3}{3*3} = 0.333$$

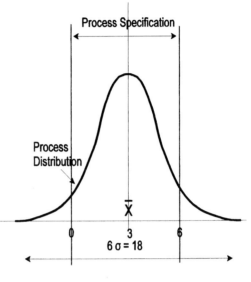

Figure 59 Interpretation of PCS results

The process is set correctly but Cpk is also an indication of spread

Process Capability Studies

Relationships Between Specifications Measurements and Process Capability

Since measurement is itself a process, it will have its own process capability. This is referred to as the uncertainty of measurement. The relationship between the process capability and the uncertainty of measurement may be appreciated in the following graphical representation.

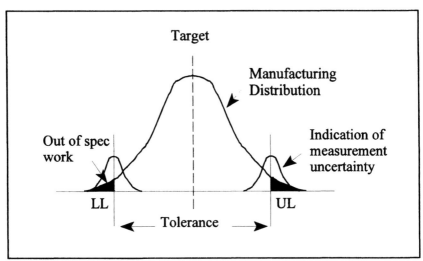

Figure 60

A number of important features may be observed:

a) The specification is the working tolerance with associated upper and lower limits.

b) Capability is the relationship between the tolerance and manufacturing distribution given as Cp or Cpk from which the areas in the tails of distribution may be calculated giving out of spec work.

c) Measurement uncertainty results in inspection error - passing defective work and failing adequate work. To ensure this error is minimal, a ratio of 10:1 between the working tolerance and measurement uncertainty is desirable.

Types of Inspection

Inspection by attributes

If inspection is limited to deciding whether an item is acceptable or not, then the form of inspection is said to be by attributes, i.e. does the item have the desired attribute or not. Attributes data is derived by counting the number or proportion of those items that do not have the desired attributes.

Examples of inspection by attributes would be:

i)   Use of a GO-NOGO[14] gauge
ii) Subjective test as to acceptability of finish compared with a sample
iii) Testing for leaks

Inspection by variables

Inspection methods that produce data that can be related to a scale such as linear dimensions; hardness; resistance; acidity etc. are referred to as inspection by variables. Obviously this data qualifies as continuous data. However, the natural limitations of the measuring instrument used will mean that the data has been grouped into discreet intervals. For instance measurements are often to the nearest unit of measurement such as 0.01 mm. or gramme.

Before proceeding, it would be useful to compare control by attributes to control by variables:

---

[14]   A gauge having two settings one of which accepts components within the specified limits and one which does not accept components outside the specified limits.

Types of Inspection

Advantages of using variables

1. Small samples (e.g. five items) are sufficient to keep a check on both process average and variability.
2. Gradual changes such as drifts can be detected and the process reset *before* it goes out of specification limit. Changes in variability can be detected on the range chart.
3. Sudden changes in process average and variability can also be detected but where this results in all work being out of specification limit, attributes will do this equally well.

Advantages of using attributes

1. Many qualities cannot be measured conveniently as variables, e.g. appearance, taste etc., although some attributes, for example sweetness, are often estimated on a scale of say 0 to 5.
2. Attributes are usually easier to check and require a less skilled inspector.
3. Several types of defective can be observed and plotted together as total number rejected, but the chart should always include an analysis, so that types which often occur can be identified and investigated.
4. Sample sizes for attributes are much larger than for variables. For example, if the scrap from a process averages 1%, a sample of 100 is needed to have an average chance of finding one reject in it and rather more to give a good chance of doing so. Samples can, and sometimes are, taken specifically to provide data for an attribute chart, but in the majority of cases we use data from 100% inspection which is being performed anyway.

Statistical Process Control

Introduction

In-process inspection means monitoring the process during production by periodically inspecting samples and plotting the results on a chart. This is called Statistical Process Control or SPC for short.

The two types of variation have already been referred to above. SPC is the application of statistics to help distinguish between variations due to common causes and those due to special causes.

If variations due to special causes occur then the process is said to be out of statistical control. If action is not taken as soon as special cause variations are indicated then rejects will occur.

The method used for SPC is the control chart. Using the results of a process capability study control limits are calculated within which all results should lie according to the rules referred to earlier.

The control chart is based on the principle that the chance of a point lying outside the control limits being due to common causes is very remote and such a point is, therefore, indicative of a special cause being present. It is, therefore, a signal to investigate the circumstances of the process to determine the reason for the special cause, to correct the condition and to identify the necessary action to prevent it from recurring in future. This may require the use of problem solving techniques such as cause-effect analysis and brain-storming which are covered later in this book.

Statistical process control (SPC) is the monitoring and analysis of process conditions using statistical techniques to determine accurately process performance and preventive or corrective actions required.

The statistical techniques involved in SPC have been around a long time, with the Shewhart control chart, designed in 1923, being little different from the type of chart in regular use today. American industry used the procedure during the Second World War in the manufacture of armaments and a British Standard entitled "Control Chart Technique" was issued in 1935. However, it is considered by many that the adoption by the Japanese of the system is the basis of their obvious success in achieving economical production.

Statistical Process Control

Many companies in the UK and elsewhere, have embraced the concepts of SPC for purely economic reasons. Unfortunately, at the time of writing, 50% of mass production in the UK has no statistical control element at all. In 35% of cases, adjustment is manually operated and only 15% is controlled automatically using closed-loop principles.

Although the theoretical concepts of SPC have been widely available for over forty years, relatively few companies have taken advantage of them until recently. In the eighties, the Ford Motor Company accelerated the application of the principles of SPC by insisting that all their contract firms adopt the concepts. Indeed they form part of QS 9000.

The emphasis by the auto manufacturers started around 1983 and, at the time, some industries felt the technique was applicable only to precision engineering parts produced in large volume. Foremost amongst these were the rubber and foundry industries. This illustrated a lack of understanding of the technique and benefits that are available to those prepared to investigate and make the necessary changes.

Unfortunately, the failure to appreciate the concepts at management level is widespread, with many organisations having little understanding of the requirements. Companies are putting systems in because their customers are demanding it, rather than from an appreciation of the benefits from their own viewpoint.

To contrast SPC and non-SPC situations, the classic study of MAZDA gearboxes provides an illustration. Some years ago, the Ford Motor Company, who have a 25% stake in Mazda, carried out a study between an American and a Japanese company manufacturing gearboxes to the same specification. The American company had twice the failure rate in the gearboxes compared to the Japanese company. On disassembling twenty gearboxes from each company and measuring the components part, it was discovered that elements from the Japanese organisation used only some 20% of the tolerance zone specified. In fact, so consistent were the measurements that it was first thought that the measuring equipment had broken down.

On the other hand, the American company's components used the whole of the tolerance zone. Whilst still being within the limits, this meant that assemblies would be outside specifications far more quickly than their Japanese counterparts. Hence, the higher failure rate encountered.

Introduction to Quality Assurance

The benefits of successful implementation are many and far-reaching. Motivation is not only a pre-condition of this success but it is a product of it. A motivation cycle can be created which will improve individual, group, department and company performance as a whole. Considerable reductions in rework costs and an almost total elimination of scrap are not unusual when SPC is operating effectively. It provides a knowledge of machine and process capability and performance, enabling the engineer to make confident decisions about equipment requirements, preventive maintenance actions and scheduling, corrective actions and cures. Prevention rather than cure is not only an important quality assurance philosophy but is the very nature of SPC. It can, therefore, reduce not only rework inspection but also first time inspection and associated costs.

Statistical Process Control

Basic ideas of control charts

Selection of the type of control chart - Variable or Attribute

Select: Decide on the most appropriate charting method to use.

Chart selection

Various types of chart are available. Described below are some of the more commonly used charts, together with examples of where the charts can be usefully employed. See **Figure 61**.

VARIABLE DATA; X/R Chart (Average and Range) These charts will be used when the data is measured, i.e. readings from measuring device such as a volt meter.

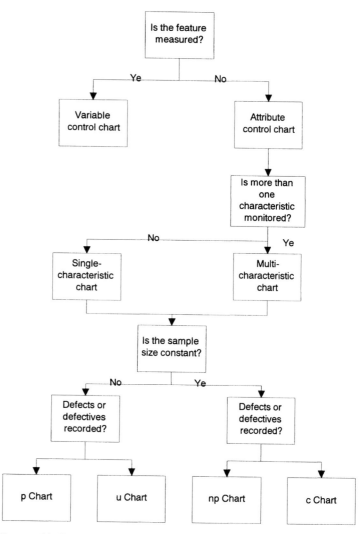

Figure 61 Chart selection

ATTRIBUTE DATA; Single characteristic chart or Multiple characteristic chart. These charts will be used in go/nogo, pass/fail situations.

i.   The p chart for proportion of defectives where the sample is not necessarily of constant size.
ii. The np chart for number of defectives where the sample size is constant.
iii. The c chart for number of defects where sample size is constant.
iv. The u chart for number of defects per Unit where the sample size is not necessarily constant.

Table 20 Attribute Chart Selection

Sample size varies	Sample size constant	Fault type	Description
Proportion	Number		
p	np	Defectives	Accept or Reject
u	c	Defects	Number of different flaws

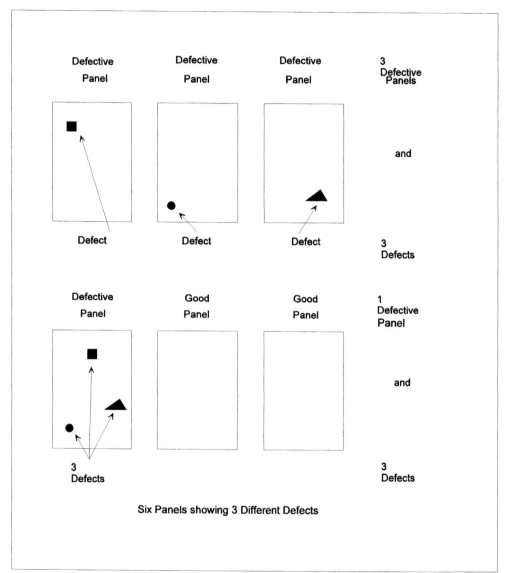

Figure 62 Defectives or Defects

Note: An item may have three different flaws; in which case there are three **defects** in the item, but there is still only one **defective** item. (See **Table 20**)

Introduction to Quality Assurance

Examples in the use of single characteristic charts may be:

For p and np types charts
- pass or fail light bulb test
- go or nogo hole size
- correct or incorrect torque loading
- accept or reject weld strength

For c or u type charts
- porosity or number of holes in a casting
- number of paint blemishes on a panel
- number of flaws in a sheet of glass
- number of errors on a printed circuit board
- number of faults with a washing machine

In the latter two examples, (printed circuit board and washing machine) each board or machine may contain various defects.

In the case of the printed circuit board the characteristics could be: a component missing, bad soldering, wrong component, defective components.

Or, in the case of the washing machine, leaking, fails to start, motor defective, heater defective etc.

In these circumstances, it may be appropriate to employ a multiple characteristic chart. With this type of chart, each of the above characteristics will be monitored individually. The result of this monitoring is then collated and the total number of defects is plotted.

Statistical Process Control

Setting up of Control Charts

Once process capability has been established and accepted, the CONTROL CHARTS need to be set up to enable monitoring of the process, with a view to maintaining quality over long periods.

Since there are two ways that processes may vary - range and mean - it is necessary to set up two separate control charts.

As with capability studies, the use of tables and set procedures will simplify the operation of control chart construction without becoming heavily involved with statistical theoretical concepts.

Procedure:

1. Initially, 'first off', at least 10 items should be produced and inspected to enable the process to be set up. A mini capability study could be achieved if computer controlled. Fifteen articles may be produced straight off, with no interval, for this purpose.

2. Initial control limits may be calculated from the capability study. These limits will be re-calculated as production proceeds.

3. The next stage is to take 20 sets of say five samples from which the control limits can be re-calculated.

4. Control limits are set as tightly as possible consistent with economic considerations. If the Cpk is very good, increase production, speeds, feeds, etc. Experiment where possible.

5. Having established the control chart, samples are next taken at regular intervals and plotted on the chart, after which the results are analysed and action to effect continuous control is taken.

6. The specification limits are never placed on the control charts - regular Cp and Cpk verification should be carried out and checks made from plotted values to see whether the process is under statistical control. In this case, the process should be well within specification limits.

7.   Where doubt exists on a plotted value a note must always be made with respect to possible causes for the freak value. Further samples may be taken immediately.

8.   It is sometimes a mistake for samples to be taken regularly as a regularly occurring error in production may be missed.

Statistical Process Control

Control Charts for Attributes

Introduction

The quality of many products is dependant upon characteristics which cannot be measured as variables. These are called attributes and may be judged simply as either present or absent, acceptable or defective. Such properties as bubbles of air in a windscreen, the general appearance of a paint surface, the particles of contamination in a sample of polymer, and the number of clerical errors in an invoice, are all attribute parameters. It is clearly not possible to use the methods of measurement and control for variables when addressing the problem of attributes.

The statistical behaviour of attribute data is different from that of variable data and this must be taken into account when designing process control systems for attributes. To examine which type of data distribution is applicable, it is necessary to know something about the product form and attribute being inspected. The following classes lead to the use of different types of control chart which are based on different statistical distributions:

1. A product in discrete units each of which can be classified as acceptable or defective, e.g. ball bearings.

2. A product in discrete units which may possess a certain number of defects, e.g. a table top.

When a fixed sample from the first type of product is inspected, for example one hundred ball bearings, it is possible to state how many are defective. It is then possible to quickly work out how many are acceptable. So in this case, if two ball bearings are found to be defective (they can also be called 'non-conformities' or 'non-conforming items'), 98 will be acceptable. This is different to the second example. If a product is examined, such as a windscreen and found to have four defects - scratches or bubbles - it is not possible to make any statements about how many scratches/bubbles are not present. This type of defect data is similar to the number of goals scored in a football match. We can only report the number of goals scored, we are unable to report how many were not.

Introduction to Quality Assurance

The two types of attribute data lead to the use of two types of control chart:

1.   Number of defective chart.

2.   Number of defects chart.

These are further split into two charts, one for the situation in which the sample size (number of units inspected) is constant, and one for samples of varying size. Hence the collection of charts for attributes becomes:

1a.   Number of defective (np) chart - for constant sample size.
1b.   Proportion defective (p) chart - for samples of varying size.
2a.   Number of defects (c) chart - for samples of same size every time.
2b.   Number of defects per unit (u) chart - for varying sample size.

Process control can be exercised using these simple charts on which the number or proportion of defectives, or the number of defects or defects per unit are plotted. Before commencing to do this, however, it is absolutely vital to clarify what constitutes a defective and what is meant by a defect. No process control technique can survive the heated arguments which will surround a badly defined system. It is evident that in the study of attribute data, there will be several degrees of imperfection. The classification of defects is a subject in its own right, but it is clear that a scratch on a paintwork or table top surface may range from a deep gouge to a slight mark, hardly visible to the naked eye. To ensure the smooth control of a process using attribute data, it is often necessary to provide representative samples, photographs or other objective evidence to support the decision make. These will allow the attention and the effort to be concentrated on improving the process rather than debating the issues surrounding defect levels.

As there is no range of values to consider with attributes, only one control chart is necessary.

The chart is set up by calculating the mean number of defectives over a period of time and by using a standard formula ascertaining the control limits. The data will also be plotted to see if the process is in statistical control at the time. Subsequently, values are plotted in the same way as variables, the information being analysed and acted upon.

Where the process is in statistical control the average level of defectives will become the capability of the process and is used as a yardstick by which improvement may be made.

Statistical Process Control

Sample size and frequency of sampling

As the attribute chart is particularly useful where 100 per cent inspection is being done the question of a sample size does not always arise. When samples are taken however, we must think in terms of much larger samples than we would use for variables and, curiously enough, the better the average quality the larger the sample size. Thus, suppose that about ten per cent of our production is usually defective. Now that it is one defective in 10, so that if a sample of, say, 20 is taken, on average two defectives per sample would be expected.

Suppose, however, the quality is improved so that only one per cent of our production is defective. Now that is only one defective in 100 and, therefore, a sample of 20 would be useless. It would only average one defective in every five samples. A sample of nearer 200 would be needed. As a general guide, the sample taken, must be large enough to give a small number of percentage of defectives to plot.

Practical considerations usually decide the frequency of inspection. Work is often produced in batches and, therefore, one sample per batch can be taken. If production is continuous, then each morning or afternoon may be treated as a batch, or make one's shift work into a batch, and so on. The principle of sampling as often as is reasonably practicable still holds. Indeed one of the disadvantages of taking a day's production as the sample is that the whole lot may be wrong before the chart draws attention to it.

Example

Consider a company making jam tarts: What may be wrong with a jam tart?

1.　　Under filled with jam.
2.　　Over filled with jam.
3.　　Crust broken.
4.　　Burnt.
5.　　Underdone.

Suppose they are manufactured in batches of 300.

Inspectors will determine on a basis of 'attributes' if the tarts are passed or failed individually.

Introduction to Quality Assurance

If the of proportion defectives in each batch (n) is 'p', e.g. 0.01, then the number of defectives in each batch will be np, e.g. 300 x 0.01 = 3. Long term, the average np may be calculated and a number attribute control chart drawn up with control limits based upon $\sigma = \sqrt{npq}$, the spread of defectives approximating to a normal distribution.

Attribute failures tend to follow a Poisson or binomial distribution which in application approximate to a normal distribution.

For example, consider a sample of 300 items; components on a printed circuit board (PCB), jam tarts, soldered joints, rivets, welds, chocolate bars. If the probability of each being good is say 0.98, i.e. q = 0.98, the probability of each being bad is 1-0.98 = 0.02.

If the binomial equation $(q + p)^{300}$ is expanded a series is produced which, when substituting the values for q and p would plot out to an approximate normal distribution:

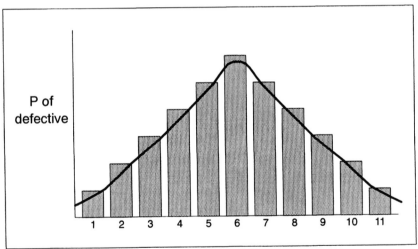

Figure 63

Probabilities beyond 11 would be negligible.
Thus it may be concluded that a control chart may be set up similar to a variables means chart.

Statistical Process Control

Proportion defective charts (p chart)

The p chart is used when dealing with defectives (e.g. scrap or rejects), and the sample size varies. In almost any production shop, the number produced varies slightly from day-to-day, so if the results of 100% inspection of daily production are monitored by a control chart, the 'sample' size varies correspondingly. The steps to set up this chart are in principle the same as used for variables charts.

Number defective (np) charts BS 5701

Probably a simpler way of plotting control limits on number defective control charts is to use the tables in BS 5701. There follows a worked example from the standard including the use of the special tables. (Questions on the IQA A11 examination paper on np charts are likely to require this method.)

The first control chart

a)   For the first trial of a number defective quality control chart, select a process that can be expected to give reasonably continuous production and that produces output containing an expected proportion of defectives in the range 1% to 10%.

b)   Select samples each of 25 items (or of 50 items if the general level of defectives in the product is 5% or less and the rate of production permits) from the most suitable point in the process. The interval between samples should be such that approximately 5% of the product is selected for examination.

c)   Examine each item, note the number of defective specimens in each sample and record this number in the order in which the samples were taken, on a control chart as shown in **Figure 64**.

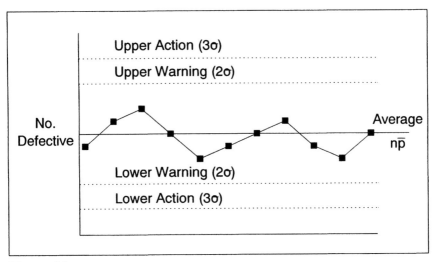

Figure 64

d)   Example:

(i)   When the results from 25 samples (each of 25 or 50 items) have been plotted in this way, find the control limit, as shown below, and mark it boldly as a broken line on the control chart.

To find the control limit:

(1)   calculate the average number of defective items ('defectives') per sample in these 25 samples,

(2)   refer to the table, the control limit will be shown against the average number of defectives per sample.

(ii)   For example, the following results of the first 25 samples, each of 50 items, taken from a production unit might be:

(1)   Number of defectives found per sample = 1, 0, 3, 0, 3, 2, 0, 2, 0, 2, 0, 1, 1, 0, 2, 5, 3, 1, 1, 2, 0, 2, 1, 1, 3.

then:

Average number of defectives $= \dfrac{36}{25} = 1.44$ per sample

(2)   On referring to the table, the control limit given for 1.53 (i.e. the number in the table next greater than the calculated number) defectives per sample is 5.7 and a broken line is placed on the chart at 5.7 defectives in a sample.

When the control limit has been placed on the chart, continue to select and examine samples, as before, recording on the chart the number of defectives found in each sample. While these recorded results remain below the control limit, variations in results should be ignored as being due to chance, and confidence may be felt that the quality of the product is not deteriorating. There is the separate question of whether this quality is satisfactory, and the states of 'in statistical control' and 'satisfactory production quality' should not be confused.

It is recommended that annotations should be made at the appropriate places on the chart to indicate occurrences of technical importance such as machine adjustment, tool replacement, change of operator, fresh supply of raw material, etc., as these notes will help the correct appraisement of trouble if results fall outside limit values.

If a result falls beyond the control limit it is a signal that the quality of the product has deteriorated and that immediate corrective action is required. If, moreover, results that usually fall below the control limit approach it and cluster near it, this is also an indication of a deterioration in quality which, if unchecked, is likely to become serious. To make this indication simpler to detect, a warning limit may be set one unit below the control limit. The presence of several points between these limits in a short period of time can be used to signal the need for investigation.

Introduction to Quality Assurance

Below are some worked examples of mean and upper & lower control limits

a. The sampled size varied but not more than ±25%[15] and on average was 500. From a total of 12000 sampled, 400 defectives were found.

The proportion of defectives is p i.e. the number of defectives (np) divided by the number in the sample.

$$\bar{p} = \frac{\Sigma np}{\Sigma n} \qquad (8)$$

Calculate the average number of defectives for the process

$$\bar{p} = \frac{Total \ number \ defectives}{Total \ number \ inspected}$$

$$\bar{p} = \frac{400}{12000} = 0.033 \qquad (9)$$

Calculate the Control Limits (UCL, LCL).

$$UCL_p = \bar{p} + 3 * \sqrt{\frac{\bar{p}(1-\bar{p})}{n}}$$

$$UCL_p = 0.033 + 3 * \sqrt{\frac{0.033(1-0.033)}{500}}$$

$$UCL_p = 0.033 + 0.024 \qquad (10)$$

$$UCL_p = 0.057$$

$$LCL_p = 0.033 - 0.024$$

$$LCL_p = 0.009$$

---

[15] If the sample size had varied more than 25%, then on each occasion the control limits should be recalculated using the sample size of the particular sub-group

Statistical Process Control

b.   100 defectives were found in twenty five samples of 60 items.

Calculate the average number of defectives in each sub-group for the process

$$\overline{np} = \frac{\Sigma np}{m}$$

$$\overline{np} = \frac{100}{25} = 4 \qquad\qquad (11)$$

Where m = The number of sub-groups

Calculate the Control Limits (UCL, LCL).

$$UCL_{np} = \overline{np} + 3 * \sqrt{\overline{np}(1 - \frac{\overline{np}}{n})}$$

$$UCL_{np} = 4 + 3 * \sqrt{4(1 - \frac{4}{60})}$$

$$UCL_{np} = 4 + 5.8 \qquad\qquad (12)$$

$$UCL_{np} = 9.8$$

$$LCL_{np} = 4 - 5.8$$

$$LCL_{np} = -1.8$$

If the LCL is negative then ignore this control limit since it is not possible to have less than zero defectives

c.   100 defects were found in ten samples of 25 items

Calculate the average number of defects in each sub-group for the process

$$\overline{c} = \frac{\Sigma c}{m}$$

$$\overline{c} = \frac{100}{10} = 10 \qquad\qquad (13)$$

Where m = The number of sub-groups

Calculate the Control Limits (UCL, LCL).

$$UCL_c = \bar{c} + 3 * \sqrt{c}$$
$$UCL_c = 10 + 3 * \sqrt{10}$$
$$UCL_c = 10 + 9.49$$
$$UCL_c = 19.49 \qquad \qquad (14)$$
$$LCL_c = 10 - 9.49$$
$$LCL_c = 0.51$$

d.   The sample size varied but not more than ±25% from a target of 8. From a total of 96 sampled, 192 defects were found.

Calculate the average number of defects in each sub-group for the process

$$\bar{u} = \frac{\Sigma c}{\Sigma n}$$
$$\bar{u} = \frac{192}{96} = 2 \qquad \qquad (15)$$

Where c = The number of defectives in each sub-grou s

Calculate the Control Limits (UCL, LCL).

$$UCL_u = \bar{u} + 3 * \sqrt{\frac{u}{n}}$$
$$UCL_u = 2 + 3 * \sqrt{\frac{2}{8}}$$
$$UCL_u = 2 + 1.5 \qquad \qquad (16)$$
$$UCL_u = 3.5$$
$$LCL_u = 2 - 1.5$$
$$LCL_u = 0.5$$

Statistical Process Control

Control chart exercise

Questions

Why is it not advisable to show the process specification or tolerance on the control charts for variables?

If the tolerance limits are to be shown on performance based variable charts how should they be shown?

What are the upper and lower control limits for variable and attribute charts based on and why is this method selected?

Answers

Why is it not advisable to show the specification tolerance on the control charts for variables?

> *Because the average value of the samples taken is plotted not the actual value. This has the effect of reducing variation or compressing the values by a factor of ;*

$$\frac{1}{\sqrt{n}}$$

> *Where n is the number in the sample*

> *The consequence of this would be that all values would appear to be within tolerance, when this may not be the case.*

If the tolerance limits are to be shown on performance based variable charts how could they be shown?

> *Either by using tolerance based control charts where the control limits are calculated by;*

Upper or Lower Control Limit $=$ Specification Limit $\pm\ 3*\dfrac{\sigma}{\sqrt{n}}$

$$\text{Where } \sigma = \text{The standard deviation of the process}$$
$$n = \text{Sample size}$$
$$\sigma_n = \text{Standard deviation of the average of the samples}$$

.

Or by showing the tolerance as a corrected tolerance;

$$\frac{Tolerance}{\sqrt{n}}$$

on performance based control charts

What are the upper and lower control limits for variable and attribute charts based on and why is this method selected?

The mean ± 3 standard deviation, because there is approximately a one in a thousand chance of a value being outside these values which indicates an improbable event.

Product Protection

Many quality problems stem from lack of controls with respect to handling, storing, packaging and transporting.

Handling may apply at any stage of the process whether it be during a process or between processes. Very often products are transported in skips or boxes with no attempt to protect them from damage.

Electronic components are particularly prone to damage through poor handling. Electro-sensitive-devices (ESDs) are components which may be damaged or destroyed by static electricity.

Human beings are very easily charged with static electricity by the combination of their movement and clothing such as nylon. We are all familiar with the electric shock we get when stepping out of a car having nylon seat covers. Such discharges would do irreversible damage to ESDs. For this reason, processes involving electrical components must be subject to strict application of 'clean room' working environment. Since dry air contributes to static electricity, this means controlling the air humidity. It also means that operators must wear earthed wrist straps while working to prevent them from building up static charges. Entrances to such areas must have earthed 'tacky mats' to discharge people entering the area and also attracting any dust or contamination which might damage components.

People are also carriers of dust and grease. Our skin and hair are continuously renewing and, therefore, shedding microscopic particles which can be devastating for certain components. The perspiration from our bodies is acidic and careless handling of components can cause corrosion and ultimate failure.

While goods are held in stores it might be thought that no harm can come to them. However, lack of control of storage conditions can result in deterioration such as temperature, humidity, cleanliness, cross contamination and shelf life.

Bonded and Quarantine Stores

Another potential problem with stores is the inadvertent or unauthorised use of items subject to controlled use or release. To prevent this, bonded stores are used. Access to bonded stores is restricted to authorised personnel. The stores are secured under lock and key.

Quarantine means to isolate. Quarantine stores are not necessarily physically restricted with respect to access and may even simply be an area set aside such as a specific shelf or area marked out on the floor. Goods found to be non-conforming or defective should be placed in a quarantine area until such time as a decision is made as to what is to happen to them.

Consumer Protection

The term is used here in the context of protecting the consumer from injury or harm as a result of hazardous or safety critical products.

The Control of Substances Hazardous to Health Regulations 1988 (COSHH) requires us to identify such and to minimise their threat. This can be achieved in a variety of ways:

iii) Eliminate the risk by substituting less hazardous materials.

iv) Minimise exposure to the risk by guarding or otherwise shielding the hazardous source.

v) Identifying the product as hazardous together with explanatory documentation

Where potential risks exist there should be:

i) Risk analysis. Techniques are available to carry out such studies to identify and minimise the risk, e.g. HAZOP (Hazard and Operability study), HACCP (Hazard and Critical Control Points study), FMECA (Failure Mode Effect and Criticality Analysis), Fault Tree Analysis etc.

ii) Disaster Recovery Procedures. This refers to the procedures necessary to have in place in the event of a serious quality failure exposing the customer or the public to risk. Examples of this include but are not limited to: food poisoning, contaminated product, incompatible product and safety critical products.

Product traceability can be rather complex. Usually, it simply means being able to trace where a product or material originated. This is backward traceability. However, forward traceability can be even more important but is much more difficult to achieve.

Product Protection

Take, for example, the case of the haemophiliacs who, in the late 80's were transfused with blood which was found to be HIV positive. Once the batch had been identified it was possible to trace its source to the blood banks of California. However, it was not possible to trace where the blood had been distributed to. At that time the procedures did not provide for forward traceability.

Car sales and domestic white goods are other examples of products containing safety critical components but almost impossible to trace where they have gone to after the initial sale. The common approach here is to issue recall notices in the media appealing to owners to return their goods for rectification. Of course such procedures are only effective if the specific goods affected can be identified. This means that the precise start and finish times of the production run are known, this is usually associated with a change of design, method of manufacture/assembly or supplier and the products are clearly identified with a serial number linking them to the affected batch.

iii) Adequately marking of safety critical goods. (For more on this topic see section on CE marking).

Inspection

Introduction

In earlier sections it was possible to see that the role of inspection has changed from that of detection to an element of control. That is not to say that defectives found are ignored. Next to be considered, in more detail, is the role of inspection.

Definition

Inspection is the process of measuring, examining, testing, gauging or otherwise comparing an item with the applicable requirements.

The inspection function is therefore concerned with:

1. Interpreting the specification or requirement.
2. Measurement of the particular characteristic.
3. Comparing (1) with (2).
4. Judging conformance.
5. Disposing of conforming cases.
6. Disposing of non-conforming cases.
7. Recording the data obtained.

Inspection may be used for a number of purposes, each aimed at improving quality:

a. To distinguish acceptable items from unacceptable items.
b. To distinguish acceptable lots from unacceptable lots.
c. To determine if the process is changing.
d. To rate the quality of a process (process average).
e. To rate the accuracy of inspectors or operators.
f. To measure the precision of a measuring instrument.
g. To measure the process capability.

Inspection

Inspection Techniques

There are three basic inspection techniques which can be used;

- sorting or judgmental inspection,
- detection inspection - informative inspection and
- preventive inspection - source inspection.

Sorting Inspection - is a sorting process which segregates the defects from the acceptable items. This action prevents defects from being received by the customer but does not prevent further defects from being made. This is the traditional approach.

Detection Inspection - is an investigation of the causes of defective items with the objective of eventually taking corrective action to prevent recurrence.

Preventive Inspection - is inspection of the potential causes of defects preventing sources of defect occurring, avoiding the production of defects in the first place. Poka-yoke may be considered one method which could be employed to achieve this objective, i.e. automatically 100% inspecting or eliminating the potential causes of defects.

There are three stages or elements to the Preventive Inspection approach:
- An understanding of the factors that can cause the defects.
- Fail safe techniques which prevent the factor which cause defects.
- Immediate action which stops the process in the event of a mistake being made, until the causes of the mistake are understood and fail safe mechanisms are established.

Inspection errors

There are a number of potential inspection errors and Juran spoke of three: technique, inadvertent and willful errors. Nikkan Kogyo Shimbun speaks of ten: forgetfulness, misunderstanding, identification, amateurs, willful, inadvertent, slowness, lack of standard, surprise and intentional errors. Philip Crosby talks of two: lack of knowledge and lack of attention all other errors are as a result of these two types. Confused? Well it may not matter too much as long as error causes are understood and an approach is adopted to prevent errors occurring.

Introduction to Quality Assurance

Types of errors

Forgetful errors - Absent-mindedness can happen for a number of reasons: lack of concentration, a moment's inattention could cause an error to occur. Possible prevention methods are; check lists, automatic safe guards, work reorganisation. Poka Yoke.

Misunderstanding - It is easy to misconstrue instructions or commands if they are not clear (*"Into the valley of death rode the five hundred"*) and as a consequence, take the wrong action. Possible prevention methods are; written instructions, training, first off checks.

Wrong Identification - Wrong categorisation or designation of an item, file or quantity can result in expensive errors. Clear methods of identification need to be established;. tagging or labelling, colour coding (although one in ten are colour blind to some degree), photographs, examples etc.

Lack of Experience - Lack of preparation for tasks and activities not only extends the start up time but also makes errors more likely. Possible prevention methods include: induction training, improved selection procedures, skill building, certification of inspectors, competent employees.

Willful Errors - Intentional errors can occur either due to deliberate mistakes or just because the rules were ignored. Possible prevention methods include: education, discipline.

Possible defect causes;

Listed are just some possible defect causes. These defect causes have been analysed with the different types of error to determine if there are any strong links.

Possible defect causes

Omitted operation	Faulty processing	Wrong location
Missing parts	Wrong part	Equipment adjustment fault
Incorrect set up	Faulty equipment	

Comparison of Error Types with Causes

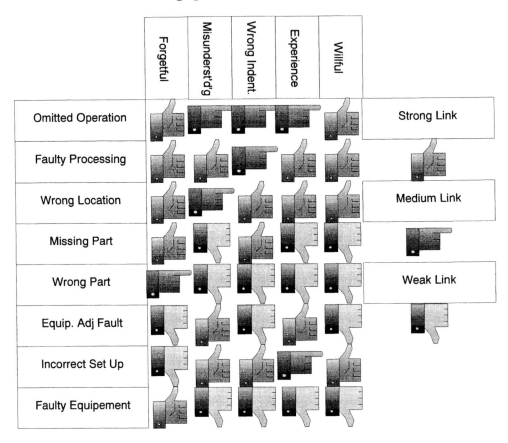

Figure 65 Relationship Matrix

Inspection Planning

As products and services have become more complex and as the job of providing them has been divided among many departments, the job of inspection has also become complex and divided. Most inspection is now done by inspectors who lack full understanding of fitness for use. For this more complex work, it has been found necessary to engage in formal inspection planning, i.e. preparing a written plan of what to inspect for and how.

Method

1. The planner visits the various locations, interviews the key people, observes the activities, and records his findings in the form of a flow diagram.

2. Selection is then made of the inspection station, e.g.

    Receipt Inspection - at movement of goods and materials between companies, usually at Goods Inwards
    First-off inspection - before starting a costly or irreversible operation.
    Process inspection - at movement of goods between departments of critical processes.
    Final inspection - upon completion of the product.

3. Inspection instructions are prepared which tell the inspector:

    a. Which features to check.
    b. How to decide whether an item conforms or not.
    c. What to do with conforming and non-conforming items.
    d. Who to inform about non-conformity.
    e. What records to make.

4. Inspection procedures are compiled.

    The inspector needs to be told how to carry out the inspection and what instruments or gauges to use.

5. Suitable documentation for inspection records is designed.

    In addition to inspection planning for production, it may also be useful to consider inspection planning for such activities as:

Inspection

Internal handling	-	use of correct containers and other handling facilities, product protection against corrosion and damage, etc.
Internal storage	-	adequate identity and traceability.
Packing	-	product identification, traceability, protection against environments, completeness, etc.
Shipping	-	care in loading, special markings, etc.

How much inspection?

The amount of inspection required at any stage is largely dependent on prior knowledge of previous experience.

1. Prior knowledge of the process:

    a. In many cases the process is so inherently stable that a first-off and last-off check is sufficient, e.g. press operations.

    b. If the process capability is known it is sufficient to take samples at intervals known to be well within the time taken for the process to change, i.e. use of control charts.

    c. Operators or suppliers who have earned a reputation for high conformity obviously require less inspection than those who lack such records.

2. Product fluidity/continuity.

    Once it has been established that a fluid or continuous product is satisfactorily homogeneous, it is necessary only to take small samples which need not be random, e.g. a short length of steel from the end of a long bar.

3. Non-critical features.

    When deciding how much inspection the consequences of too little inspection must be considered. Obviously some features will not be critical and, therefore, not require regular inspection, e.g. non-functional dimensions.

Obtaining prior knowledge may require some effort on the part of the inspection planner. Such information may not always be readily available and may require special tests or experiments.

Decision making on fitness for use

It is necessary to give careful consideration to the delegation of decision- making about the acceptance or otherwise of items.

Case 1   The item is realistically specified in an objective manner in such a way that the item can readily be classified as fit for use or not. Such decisions can be safely delegated to the inspector or even the operator.

Case 2   The item is realistically specified but in a subjective manner such as "surface must be scratch-free". Decisions of acceptance can only be delegated to the operator or inspector providing he has an adequate means of discriminating good from bad items, e.g. samples and training sessions.

Case 3   The item is not realistically toleranced and is the subject of discretion which varies with pressures such as urgency. It is unfair to subject inspectors to varying standards and it is usual to 'draw the line' and any items non-conforming items will only be accepted as a result of the issue of a *concession note*. Such a concession note should only be issued after consultation by a committee at an appropriate level consistent with the consequences of the decision.

Control of non-conforming product

Where non-conforming items or products have been found, procedures need to be established and implemented that identify and, if appropriate, segregate the non-conforming material or product until such time as a decision can be made as to the action necessary (concessions, rework, scrap, regrade).

Evaluation of suspect material: If suspect material is found, a possible approach that can be adopted in determining what action to take is detailed in **Figure 66**:

Inspection

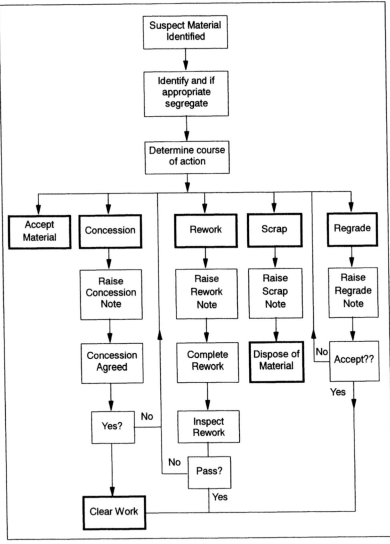

Figure 66

Computer Aided Quality Assurance

The computer has now become a common place, relatively low cost item of equipment which can have dramatic effects on productivity, particularly in the handling and manipulation of data. One of the largest activities of the Quality Department is the handling and manipulation of data and it is for this reason that the computer has been quickly adopted in the Quality Assurance environment.

Some of the reasons why the computer has been used in the quality assurance environment are:

Information	■	the sheer volume of information that the quality department handles.
Expediency	■	it is much more efficient and time saving to employ a computer to perform data processing.
Data collation	■	the manipulation, presentation, sorting and selection of data.
Archiving	■	data can be stored and retrieved, sorted and selected much more quickly.
Communication	■	the use of electronic mail can improve the speed and accuracy of information transferred between locations.

There are various types of computer available although the distinction between the different types is becoming much less clear. Main/mini frame, multi-tasking and multi-user computer systems, personal computers. These computers can also vary in terms of the operating systems employed, e.g. MS DOS, Unix, OS2, Windows etc. Sometimes, because of the various operating systems, communication between each type of machine can present problems.

Types of Software Available

Word Processor Packages - e.g. WordPerfect, Microsoft Word, etc.

Word processor packages are commercially available software programs for the production of documentation. These programs are generally menu based for 'user friendliness' and have help facilities available, i.e. they display the various options available to the user when compiling documents. Many of the word processor packages are capable of processing graphics as well as text, so can be useful for presentations. These graphical capabilities can also be used to make the quality manual presentation more acceptable and easier to use. Control of issue and amendment of the quality manual can be enhanced by the use of a word processor. Repetitive or similar documents are easier to produce (e.g. quotations, procedures etc.), with more effective archiving, retrieval and data storage etc.

Desktop publishing or Graphics packages - e.g. Harvard Graphics, Corel, Pagemaker, Microsoft Publisher etc.

Desktop publishing packages are commercially available software programs that are a highly sophisticated extension to a word processor. These software packages enable documents such as reports and material for presentations etc. to be compiled or presented in a sophisticated way which emulates the quality of magazines and books. Most word processor packages are now capable of performing many of the operations that were the exclusive province of the desktop package.

Database packages - e.g. dBASE, DataEase, Fox Pro, Access

Processing of information and data is one of the principal activities of the quality department. The data processing usually involves these basic steps: data input (paperwork), storage and retrieval system (files), processing or manipulation of data and finally an output or report.

With manual systems data manipulation can be difficult to achieve, especially if the data is required to be analysed in a different or new manner, e.g. obtaining from the calibration control system the total value of all the measuring equipment. It can be done, but it may be a lengthy process.

Flexibility is just one of the advantages that can be gained by the application of a database program. There are many others such as reduction in cost, ease of writing reports, speed of data processing etc.

What are databases? A database is a file containing all the relevant information pertaining to a particular record. In everyday life this could be analogous to an address book, telephone book or price list. On the computer, this could be a file containing information and records of all the measuring equipment in a factory.

One of the fundamental requirements of a database is to arrange data in a specific order. With a telephone directory this would be alphabetical - name, initial and then address. With a manual calibration database the usual order would be by equipment number. Having the data on a computer means that it is a relatively simple task to alter the data into numerous different sequences. For example, calibration date, withdrawal date, equipment cost, equipment name, equipment supplier etc.

This information can be sent to a printer to provide a printout of equipment records. To get the information into a database the data must be structured (see **Figure - Database for Calibration**). Each discrete piece of information is given a field such as equipment name, recall frequency, location etc.

The FIELD-HEADER is the prompt on the computer screen when the computer is expecting a response to a question, e.g. Equipment No. ?

A set of fields relating to a particular individual entity, such as an equipment type, equipment name etc. is called a **record**.

A collection of records is called a **file**, such as all the equipment in one department or all the equipments of one type (e.g. micrometers).

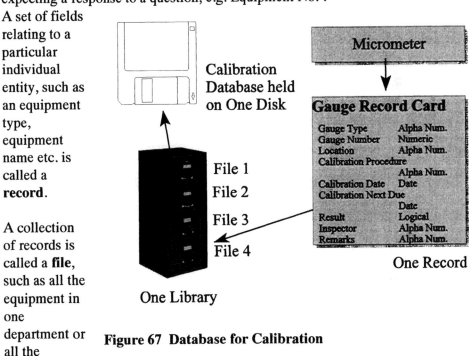

Calibration Database held on One Disk

File 1
File 2
File 3
File 4

One Library

Gauge Record Card

Gauge Type	Alpha Num.
Gauge Number	Numeric
Location	Alpha Num.
Calibration Procedure	Alpha Num.
Calibration Date	Date
Calibration Next Due	Date
Result	Logical
Inspector	Alpha Num.
Remarks	Alpha Num.

Micrometer

One Record

Figure 67 Database for Calibration

A collection of files is called a **library**, such as all the equipment in a factory.

Possible Database Applications

There are numerous applications within the quality department for a computer database. Below are listed just some applications that have been identified which may require a considerable amount of data manipulation.

Computer Aided Quality Assurance

- Calibration control
- Vendor rating or supplier management
- Product recall system
- Customer complaints analysis
- Quality problems
- Warranty Reports
- Audit Reports
- Training Records
- Document Control

Spread Sheet packages

A spread sheet program is a general purpose software package. Such a software package provides a relatively simple means of modelling certain calculations on a computer by electronic representation of calculation paper.

A spread sheet takes the form of a large sheet of paper divided into columns (usually identified by a letter) and rows (usually identified by a number). Each cell can be identified by its column and row co-ordinate, (Cell Address). Each cell can contain information such as: letters,

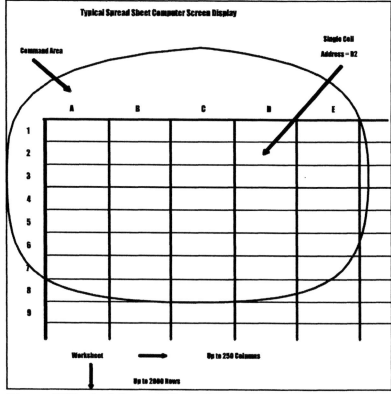

Figure 68 Typical Spread Sheet Screen Display

224

numbers or instructions. (See **Figure 68**).

Letters: Can be headers for each column or row, or labels used as a guide to the contents of a cell, e.g. Prevention Cost.

Numbers: The basic raw data or value that is going to be used in the spread sheet, e.g. amounts of money spent on prevention for a particular month.

Instructions: or formulae are used to carry out calculations or the manipulation of the data, e.g. sums all the values in column E. Possibly the total cost of quality for a particular month.

This sheet can be viewed on a monitor screen, but if the spread sheet is of any size then the whole sheet could not be displayed at the same time. The monitor screen acts as a window displaying only a section of the spread sheet at any one time. This window can be moved over the spread sheet by using the cursor control keys.

The section on the cost of quality includes a spread sheet showing the cost break down on a quarter by quarter basis. The graphs in the section cost of quality were produced from the cost of quality data using a spread sheet package.

Application for such programs could be: budgets, cash flow plans and forecasts, cost allocation, ad hoc calculations, statistical analysis and quality cost analysis. Examples of commercially available spread sheet programs for the PC include: Lotus 123, Quattro Pro and Excel.

Before entering data into the spread sheet, it is often wise to consider the most appropriate screen layout and what information to place in the spread sheet. The spread sheet can be preprogrammed so that after the data to be processed has been entered the computer will automatically calculate all the necessary factors, plot the graphs and print out the results in a report format.

It is very important that any spreadsheet model should be validated by the use of dummy data to confirm that the expected result is achieved.

Processing of Statistical Quality Control Data

Statistical Quality Control (SQC) is very easily adapted for use on the computer, this is because a considerable number of calculations are necessary in order to calculate the statistics or data required, e.g. mean and standard deviation.

Programs are now available which can calculate process capability, standard deviations etc. They can establish whether the process is capable of producing to a required specification. Subsequently, when the particular process is running, the software can calculate the data for the average and range charts and determine the position of the control limits for variable charts or the proportion of defects and control limits for attribute charts. These charts can then be displayed graphically on the computer screen and a 'hard copy' obtained from the printer for a permanent record.

The results obtained can be displayed graphically on the screen and the computer can give timely warnings of any trends which could result in material not meeting specification. For example trends which, if continued, could mean the data going outside of control limits or any other non-random or special cause of variation which is above or below the mean. (See Statistical Quality Control).

The SQC software has the ability to spot these non-random factors and draw them to the attention of the computer user. The way in which the software could be used may involve the inspector collecting the data (possibly in hand-written form), returning to the computer and feeding the data into the computer. Alternatively, electronic equipment is available which may be data linked to gauging which feeds directly into the computer, and therefore removes the necessity for manual measurement recording. This provides the ability to monitor continuously processes with immediate graphic interpretation of the data being collected.

This is obviously a vast improvement over the old methods of collecting data which had tended to rely on a detective approach to Quality Assurance. With the application of computers then a new preventive type of approach can be adopted by closely monitoring the process. The likelihood of defects being produced at some future time can be predicted so that timely corrective action can be taken.

There are a number of excellent share ware programmes available to perform statistical analysis of data, these include SPCPro and SPCEx.

Although this is a great advantage there are some major disadvantages. Where a number of different features need to be monitored then the cost of attaching electronic measuring equipment to all of these features may be prohibitively expensive. This is particularly so, where a product has a number of different features or where small batch quantities are produced. Also, the whole philosophy behind SQC is towards operator quality control. The use of an inspector and a computer removes the operator involvement. The emphasis with computer control SQC is for the inspector to gather the data, or for the inspector to do the interpretation of the graphical results. This runs totally contrary to the concepts of operators being responsible for the quality of the work they produce. Controlling the processes by means of plotting and monitoring the data, provides the operator with the opportunity for active participation in the monitoring of the quality of the work. With the computer in the quality control system, the inspection department becomes the controlling factor, shifting the emphasis and possibly responsibility for quality from production to the quality department.

Computer Controlled Equipment

CNC - Computer Numerical Control: CNC machines are computer controlled equipment generally used for the production of complicated, tight tolerance machined parts. CNC is normally used for low to medium volume production due to the programming time required. The advantages of these machines is that once programmed they will produce the same component on a highly repeatable basis.

CNC machines frequently employ multi-headed 'tool posts' (e.g. chucks) which once loaded up hold every tool required for that operation or series of operations, i.e. can reduce the number of tools and jigs required etc. Examples of CNC equipment are lathes, drilling and milling machines.

The effect of using these machines is to put the emphasis for quality control on the programming and first off inspection. It is important to ensure that the first component produced conforms to specification. Thereafter it should only be necessary to monitor for tool breakage and wear. Next time the job is run, the first off inspection on the computer programme has been completed and it may be possible to perform a much reduced inspection. Often when new computer controlled manufacturing equipment is employed it is soon discovered that much of the new equipment's time is spent in waiting for inspection from the quality department. To overcome such delays a computer aided measuring machine can be employed, reducing inspection time and improving the productivity of the computer controlled manufacturing equipment. However, what is not always appreciated is that considerable engineering support is supplied to introducing the computer aided manufacturing equipment but the same effort and support is not always given to the computer aided measuring machine; the result being that full benefit is not derived from the computer aided measuring machine.

The type of engineering support which could be provided may include; programming the measuring machine at the same time as the manufacturing machine (although there may be certain dangers with this approach - making the same programming mistake twice), provision of special purpose fixtures for holding the components. Basically planning the inspection and test activities with the same diligence as the manufacturing activities (Quality Planning).

Automatic Test Equipment - ATE: ATE equipment is computer controlled test equipment which is frequently used for the testing of (electronic) assemblies and sub-assemblies. Typically these types of machines have either an 'in circuit' or a 'functional' test capability (or a combination of these).

'In circuit' testing really confirms that a circuit board has been manufactured correctly (i.e. finds short circuits, open circuits and components that are outside tolerance limits). The in circuit tester usually interfaces with the unit under test (UUT) via a bed of nails fixture that has one pin for every electrical node. This allows measuring of characteristics between any electrical connections (e.g. across each component).

'Functional' testing interfaces to the UUTis either via a few pins in a bed of nails fixture (e.g. maybe one pin per 100 connections) or by way of flying leads. This means of testing could be used for a printed circuit board or a whole assembly. A 'good' functional test will find any manufacturing defects plus any parameters that are not within design specifications.

Functional testing is quick to highlight a failure whereas in circuit testing is quicker to pin-point where the failure lies, i.e. identifies the fault location down to component level.

ATE is typically used for medium to high volume production or where high level technology, such as the space industry, is used.

The use of automatic testing ensures that all the assemblies are tested to within predefined tolerances. The testing becomes objective as opposed to subjective. The QA personnel would need to ensure that the preselected tolerances are correct. Once proven, this method of testing provides a very high degree of repeatability plus the availability of automatically logged test results for use in SQC and real time fault analysis (RTFA).

PART D

Basic Statistical Methods

Basic Statistical Methods

Discrete and Continuous Variables

So far only discrete variables have been considered. In other words, the values vary in discrete or whole steps. In many situations the variables may vary on a continuous scale. For example, if the feet of 50 people were measured a metric scale might be used and depending on the precision of the measuring instrument end up with 50 different measurements. The probability distribution

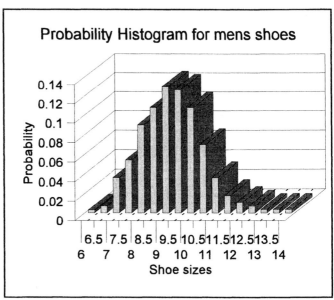

Figure 69

would therefore appear to be rectangular (one for each size). In the days of craftsmen the shoemaker might make every pair of shoes to fit the individual and thus no two pair of shoes would be identical. In these days of mass production it has been found that using discrete steps of ½ sizes of shoes is sufficient to satisfy the majority of people. Thus it would be useful to the shoemaker to have some idea of the probability distribution of the sizes of men's feet in relation to a scale of discrete steps of ½ sizes. The resulting probability distribution might be something like **Figure 70.**

Therefore, in order to have any distribution at all it is necessary to choose a suitable step when measuring a continuous variable. This step is called the **class interval**. In the absence of a natural class interval, as in the case of shoe sizes, it is usual to create a class interval based on the likely spread of the distribution divided into approximately 10 intervals.

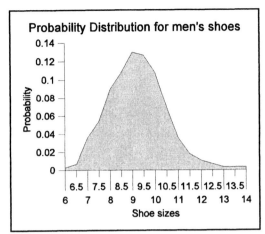

Figure 70

Another refinement of the probability distribution is to create a smooth envelope or probability distribution curve.

Probability Distribution Patterns

As seen above, probability distribution patterns can take various shapes. Typical examples found in different circumstances are presented below:

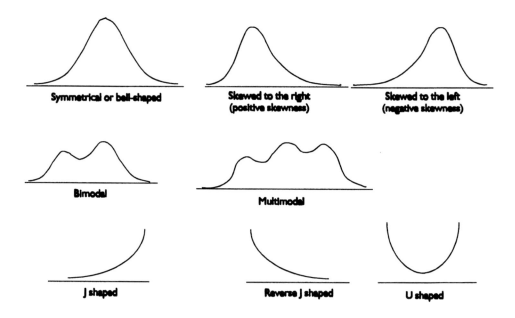

Figure 71

The distribution pattern of most interest in Statistical Quality Control is the symmetrical bell-shaped curve. The reason being that the variation of most stable processes will display such a distribution or something approximating to it. Try cutting a length of string into approximately 100 mm length just estimating and without measuring. Then construct a histogram and hence a frequency curve by smoothly joining the tops of the bars in the histogram. Cut 50 lengths then measure them accurately to the nearest mm. Do not be surprised if the curve looks something like the symmetrical bell-shaped curve.

As this curve is so central to Statistical Quality Control, it is important to explore its properties.

The Normal Distribution

The bell shaped curve referred to is called the Normal Distribution.

There are four variables to the bell shaped distribution.

(a) The position of the curve on a scale
(b) The spread of the distribution
(c) The skewness of the distribution and
(d) The peakedness of the distribution referred to as the Kurtosis

For current purposes discussion will be limited to the first two measures considering only a symmetrical bell-shaped curve.

Statistics of the Normal Distribution

1. Position

It is quite common to talk of average values. However, there are different types of average. At this stage three will be considered. The mode, the median and arithmetic mean.

a. The Mode

This is the value occurring with the most frequency. It is the value corresponding to the peak of the curve.

b. The Median

This is the mid value or the value that divides the distribution into two equal halves.

c. The Arithmetic Mean

This is the sum of the values divided by the total number of values:

$$Mean = \frac{\sum \text{ of values}}{n}$$

Note: for a Normal Distribution, the values of the Mode, Median and Mean are the same.

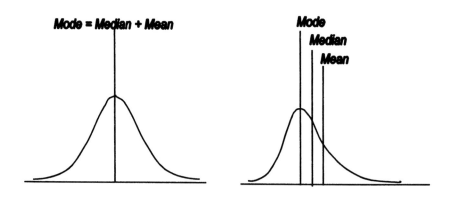

Figure 72

The Arithmetic Mean is the most common measure of distribution position.

2. Spread

The mean value does not give complete information about a population (the variable).

Consider these two samples:

Sample No 1	Bar lengths	24	23	26	27 units	$\bar{x}$ = 25
Sample No 2	Bar lengths	6	37	34	23 units	$\bar{x}$ = 25

Although in both samples the means are the same, the spreads are clearly different. Therefore, a suitable measure for spread is needed.

As with the position, a number of measures are available.

Introduction to Quality Assurance

a. The Range

The range is defined as the difference between the smallest and the greatest values. On the face of it this appears to be the best measure. However, it is difficult to be precise since the probabilities at the extremes get smaller and smaller but are not zero, so just where does the distribution start and finish?

b. The Mean Deviation

The deviations from the centre position could be averaged. However, this would mean ignoring the signs otherwise they would cancel each other out. Because of this, the value has no mathematical meaning.

c. The Variance

By squaring the deviations, the difficulty of the signs is overcome, since they all become positive when squared. If therefore, the arithmetic mean of the squares of the deviations is calculated, then the result is what is called the variance thus:

$$Variance = \frac{\sum deviations^2}{n}$$

$$Variance = \frac{\sum f(x - \bar{x})^2}{\sum f}$$

d. The Standard Deviation σ

The problem with the variance is that it is in square units. This means that while it has mathematical meaning it has no physical position on the curve. If the square root of the variance is taken, then we are back to linear units which does have a physical relationship to the distribution.

$$\sigma = \sqrt{\frac{\sum deviations^2}{n}}$$

$$\sigma = \sqrt{\frac{\Sigma f(x - \bar{x})^2}{\Sigma f}}$$

This value can be readily calculated using a scientific calculator.

Sigma σ is the most common measure of spread of the distribution.

This will now be repeated, only this time using actual figures to illustrate the manual method of calculation.

Example

x	f	fx	$(x - \bar{x})$	$(x - \bar{x})^2$	$f(x - \bar{x})^2$
100.1	3	0.3	- 0.2033	0.0413	0.1239
100.2	7	1.4	- 0.1033	0.0107	0.0749
100.3	10	3.0	- 0.0033	0.00001	0.0001
100.4	6	2.4	+ 0.0967	0.0094	0.0564
100.5	4	2.0	+ 0.1967	0.0387	0.1548
	30	9.1			0.4101

$$\bar{x} = \frac{\sum fx}{\sum f} = \frac{9.1}{30} = 0.3033 \qquad \sigma = \sqrt{\frac{\sum f(x-\bar{x})^2}{\sum f}}$$

Actual $\bar{x}$ = 100.3033

$$\sigma = \sqrt{\frac{0.4101}{30}} = 0.117$$

Properties of the Normal Distribution

Normal Distribution and Confidence Level - One of the main attractions of the normal distribution is the predictability of the percentages of values within given limits.

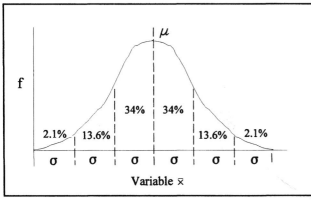

x is a variable
μ is the mean of the population.
σ is the standard deviation of the population

The area under the curve between specific values of x represents the percentage of the population within those values.

Figure 73

237

Example 1 If the mean height of the male population is 5 feet 10 inches. Then there is a 50% probability that a male person picked at random, will have a height of 5 feet 10 inches or more. Assuming that the distribution is a normal distribution, i.e. symmetrical[16]

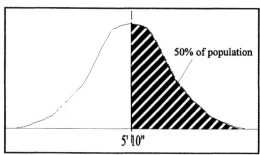
50% of population
5' 10"

Figure 74

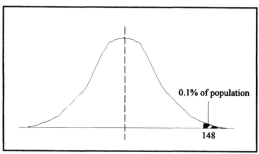
0.1% of population
148

Figure 75

Example 2 A person picked at random has an IQ of over 148 with a confidence of 99.9%.

Example 3 A person picked at random has an IQ between 84.5 and 115.5 with a confidence of 68%.

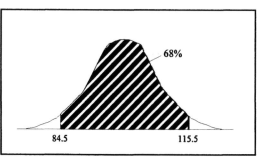
68%
84.5   115.5

Figure 76

Whatever the distribution, providing the parameters follow specific equations, the area between given limits, may be found by integration. The area represents a level of confidence. A good example in reliability would be the Mean Time Between Failures

---

[16]   The examples shown are for illustration only. Real life distributions may vary from those shown here.

(MTBF) factor, where a stated quantity might be that there is a 90% confidence of the MTBF being between 12,000 hours and 14,000 hours.

Consider some practical exercises involving the normal distribution, and areas between and outside specified limits.

Example 4 Determine the percentage of product outside the specification limit

Specification limits: 100   = ±2 units
Process capability: $\bar{x}$ = 100 σ = 0.75

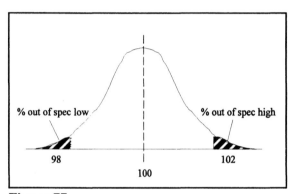

To find the area under the curve, first calculate the statistic u which is the number of standard deviations between the mean and a value x. (This is referred to as the normal deviate)

Figure 77

$$u = \frac{(x - \mu)}{\sigma}$$
$$= \frac{(102 - 100)}{0.75}$$
$$= 2.67$$

Referring now to Table 3 in *Murdoch and Barnes Statistical Tables Edition 3*, this value of u corresponds to an area under the tail of 0.00379 (0.379%). In other words 0.379% of the work is likely to be oversize.

Similarly for the lower limit:

The fact that u is negative is not important, the tables are still used in the same way. Thus 0.379% of the work will be undersize. This means that a total of 0.758% of the work will be outside the specified limits

$$u = \frac{(x - \mu)}{\sigma}$$
$$= \frac{(98 - 100)}{0.75}$$
$$= -2.67$$

Example 5

Specification limits:100   = ±3 units
Process Capability: x̄   = 101   σ = 1.5

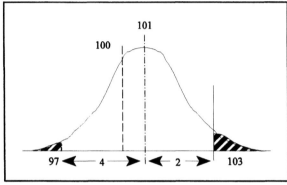

Figure 78

For the upper limit:

$$u = \frac{(x - \mu)}{\sigma}$$
$$= \frac{(101 - 100)}{1.5}$$
$$= -1.33$$

Which corresponds to an area of 0.0918 or 9.18%

For the lower limit:

$$u = \frac{(x - \mu)}{\sigma}$$
$$= \frac{(97 - 100)}{1.5}$$
$$= -2.67$$

Which corresponds to an area of 0.00379 or 0.379% giving a total of 9.559% out of specification.

The Binomial Distribution

So far variables and their distribution have been considered. For attributes the measure is a number or proportion of defects or defectives. For this reason, another type of distribution - the Binomial Distribution, will now be considered. This distribution approximates to a normal distribution and can be used to calculate probabilities of defects or defectives.

The Binomial Theorem may be used whenever a series of trials satisfies the following conditions:

(a) There are only two possible outcomes in each trial which are mutually exclusive. These outcomes may be success and failure, defective and non-defective, go or not go, etc.

(b) The probability of success in each trial is constant. The probability of success is usually denoted by p and the probability of failure is usually denoted by $q = 1 - p$.

(c) The outcomes of successive trials are mutually independent. This condition is met approximately when items are selected from a large batch and classified as defective and non-defective.

Consider at a simple practical experiment, first of all to compare statistical theory with practice, and secondly to introduce the binomial theorem.

Practical exercise

Take three coins and toss them in the air 1,000 times - note the number of occasions when there are no heads, 1 head, two heads and three heads in three using the following table:
Theoretical frequency
Probability of a head   =   H   =   1/2
Probability of a tail   =   T   =   1/2

Listing all the possibilities:

OH   T   x   T   x   T   =   ½   x   ½   x   ½ =   ⅛   =   0.125

1H   H   x   T   x   T   =   ½   x   ½   x   ½ =   ⅛ }
        T   x   H   x   T   =   ½   x   ½   x   ½ =   ⅛ } = ⅜ = 0.375
        T   x   T   x   H   =   ½   x   ½   x   ½ =   ⅛ }

2H   T   x   H   x   H   =   ½   x   ½   x   ½ =   ⅛ }
        H   x   H   x   T   =   ½   x   ½   x   ½ =   ⅛ } = ⅜ = 0.375
        H   x   T   x   H   =   ½   x   ½   x   ½ =   ⅛ }

3H   H   x   H   x   H   =   ½   x   ½   x   ½ =   ⅛ } =   <u>0.125</u>

                              Total   =   1.000

Tally chart:

Number of heads	Frequency	Total Empirical frequency	Theoretical frequency
0H (no heads)			125
1H (1 head)			375
2H (2 heads)			375
3H (3 heads)			125
		1000	1000

Formalising this a general expression for theoretical probabilities may be determined.

The formulations are: OH   TTT   = T^3 T^3

                        1H   HTT   = T^2H }
                               THT   = T^2H } $3T^2H$
                               TTH   = T^2H }

                        2H   THH   = H^2T }
                               HHT   = H^2T } $3H^2T$
                               HTH   = H^2T }

                        3H   HHH   =   H H^3

Since the combined probabilities is 1.0

T^3	$+ 3T^2H$	$+ 3TH^2$	$+ H^3$	$=$	1
T^3	$+ 3T^2H$	$+ 3TH^2$	$+ H^3$		is an expansion of $(T + H)^3$ called a binomial expansion.

The respective probabilities of OH, 1H, 2H and 3H will be the corresponding terms of the expansion $T^3 + 3T^2H + 3TH^2 + H^3$

In general, we can say that the probabilities of x heads will be

$$P_x = c_x T^{n-x} H^x$$

Where c_x is a co-efficient for the respective number of events (heads).

$$c_x = \frac{n!}{x! \, (n-1)!}$$

Where n! stands for n factorial, all numbers from 1 to n multiplied together.

e.g. $5! = 1 \times 2 \times 3 \times 4 \times 5 = 120$

$$\therefore P_x = \frac{n!}{x! \, (n-1)!} T^{n-x} H^x$$

Example: Calculate the probability of 0, 1, 2, 3, 4, 5, heads when tossing 5 coins.

$$T+H) = \frac{5!}{0!\,(5-0)!}T^{5-0}H^0 + \frac{5!}{1!\,(5-1)!}T^{5-1}H^1 + \frac{5!}{2!\,(5-2)!}T^{5-2}H^2$$
$$+ \frac{5!}{3!\,(5-3)!}T^{5-3}H^3 + \frac{5!}{4!\,(5-4)!}T^{5-4}H^4 + \frac{5!}{x!\,(5-5)!}T^{5-5}H^5$$
$$= \frac{5!}{0!5!}T^5H^0 + \frac{5!}{1!4!}T^4H^1 + \frac{5!}{2!\,3!}T^3H^2 + \frac{5!}{3!\,2!}T^2H^3 + \frac{5!}{4!\,1!}T^1H^4 + \frac{5!}{5!\,0!}T^0H^5$$
$$= T^5 + \frac{120}{24}T^4H^1 + \frac{120}{2\times6}T^3H^2 + \frac{120}{6\times2}T^2H^3 + \frac{120}{24}T^1H^4 + H^5$$
$$= T^5 + 5T^4H^1 + 10T^3H^2 + 10T^2H^3 + 5T^1H^4 + H^5$$
$$= 0.5^5 + 5\times0.5^4\times0.5^1 + 10\times0.05^3 0.5^2 + 10\times0.5^2 0.5^3 + 5\times0.5^1 0.5^4 + 0.5^5$$
$$= 0.03125 + 0.15625 + 0.3125 + 0.3125 + 0.15625 + 0.03125$$

$(T + H)^5$ comes out as:

OH	1H.	2H	3H	4H	5H		
32.15	156.25	312.5	312.5	156.25	31.25	for	1,000 trials (tosses)

Ex. Calculate the probability of 0 or 1 heads

0.03125	OH
0.15625	1H
0.18750	

Ex. Calculate the probability of 0, 1 or 2 heads

0.03125	OH
0.15625	1H
0.31250	2H
0.50000	

Instead of using formulae to ascertain the binomial co-efficients, providing the expansion is symmetrical the binomial co-efficients can be found by using Pascals triangle as follows:

Introduction to Quality Assurance

Value of n   Numerical co-efficients in the expansion of $(p + q)^n$

Pascals Triangle

```
                    1
1                1   1
2              1   2   1
3            1   3   3   1
4          1   4   6   4   1
5        1   5  10  10   5   1
6      1   6  15  20  15   6   1
7    1   7  21  35  35  21   7   1
8  1   8  28  56  70  56  28   8   1
```

Notice that the construction of this chart is based on each number being the sum of the two numbers above it, i.e. referring to the bottom row $1 = 0 + 1, 8 = 1 + 7, 28 = 7 + 21$ etc.

In quality control the symbols Q and P are used. Q for a good component P for a defective component. When $Q = P = 0.5$ the results are similar to $(T + H)^n$ where $T = H = 0.5$.

When the probabilities of success and failure are equal (0.5) then a symmetrical distribution which approximates to the normal distribution is produced.

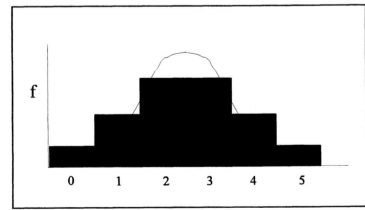

Figure 79

In practice, it is realistic to assume that the defectives in a sample or batch will be quite small, e.g. say $Q = 0.9$ $P = 0.1$

Basic Statistical Methods

Example 1

It is known that 10% of the resistors produced by a certain process are defective. From a large batch a sample of five resistors is taken at random. Find the probabilities of obtaining 0, 1, 2, 3, 4 and 5 defective resistors in the sample and draw a histogram to represent these probabilities.

The probability of a single resistor, chosen at random, being defective is

$$p = \frac{10}{100} = 0.1$$

The probability of it being good is $\qquad q = 1 - p = 0.9$
The number in the sample is $\qquad n = 5$

Now $\qquad (q + p)^5 = q^5 + 5q^4p + 10q^3p^2 + 10q^2p^3 + 5qp^4 + p^5$

The probabilities are shown in the table below and the histogram that follows.

Number of defectives in the sample	Term of expansion	Probability	
12345	q^5	$(0.9)^5$	$= 0.59049$
	$5q^4p$	$5 \times (0.9)^4 \times (0.1)$	$= 0.32805$
	$10q^3p^2$	$10 \times (0.9)^3 \times (0.1)^2$	$= 0.07290$
	$10q^2p^3$	$10 \times (0.9)^2 \times (0.1)^3$	$= 0.00810$
	$5qp^4$	$5 \times (0.9) \times (0.1)^4$	$= 0.00045$
	p^5	$(0.1)^5$	$= 0.00001$

Total probability covering all possible   events $= 1.00000$

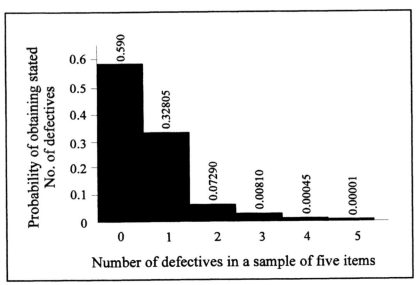

Figure 80

Example 2

Cartons which contain four items each are checked and it is found that 8% of the items are defective. If 10,000 cartons are purchased find:

a)   How many cartons are expected to have no defective items.
b)   How many cartons are expected to have one defective item.
c)   How many cartons are expected to have less than two defective items.
d)   How many defective items there are likely to be in the 10,000 cartons.

Solutions

a)   If one carton is selected at random then the probability of it containing no defective items is given by the first term of $(q + p)^4$ which is q^4. Since $p = 0.08$, then $q = 0.92$ and $q^4 = (0.92)^4 = 0.7164$ the number of cartons containing no defective items is expected to be $0.7164 \times 10,000 = 7,164$.

b)   The probability of finding a carton with one defective item in it is the second term of $(q + p)^4$, i.e. $4q^3p = 4 \times (0.92)^3 \times 0.08 = 0.2492$. The number of cartons with 1 defective item is expected to be $0.2492 \times 10,000 = 2,492$.

c)   The number of cartons containing less than two defective items (i.e. containing no defective items or containing one defective item) is expected to be 7,164 + 2,492 = 9,656.

d)   The number of defective items in the 10,000 boxes is expected to be 4 x 10,000 x 0.08 = 3,200.

Example 3

A machine is known to produce 10% of defective parts. Samples of four items are taken from the batches produced and examined. If 1,000 samples are checked, draw a histogram showing the number of defectives which are to be expected.

Here $p = 0.1$, $q = 1 - p = 0.9$ and $n = 4$.

$$(q + p)^4 = q^4 + 4q^3p + 6q^2p^2 + 4q^2p^2 + 4qp^3 + p^4$$

The distribution is shown in the following table:

Number of defectives in the sample	Term of the binomial expansion	Probability of the stated number of defectives being found in the sample		Number of samples with the stated number of defectives	
0	q^4	$(0.9)^4$	= 0.656	1,000 x 0.656	= 656
1	$4q^3p$	$4 \times (0.9)^3 \times (0.1)$	= 0.292	1,000 x 0.292	= 292
2	$6q^2p^2$	$6 \times (0.9)^2 \times (0.1)^2$	= 0.049	1,000 x 0.049	= 49
3	$4qp^3$	$4 \times (0.9) \times (0.1)^3$	= 0.003	1,000 x 0.003	= 3
4	p^4	$(0.1)^4$	= 0.0001	1,000 x 0.0001	= 0.1

Introduction to Quality Assurance

The histogram below represents the distribution.

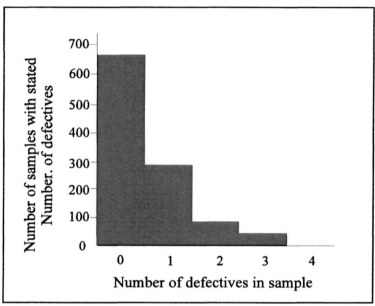

Figure 81

Example 4

Eight coins are tossed together 256 times. Draw up a theoretical frequency table for the number of heads which may be expected and hence construct a histogram to represent the theoretical frequency distribution.

Here $p = \frac{1}{2}$, $q = \frac{1}{2}$ and $n = 8$

$$(q + p)^8 = q^8 + 8q^7p + 28q^6p^2 + 56q^5p^3 + 70q^4p^4 + 56q^3p^5 + 28q^2p^6 + 8qp^7 + p^8$$

The histogram of the theoretical frequencies distribution is shown in **Figure 82**

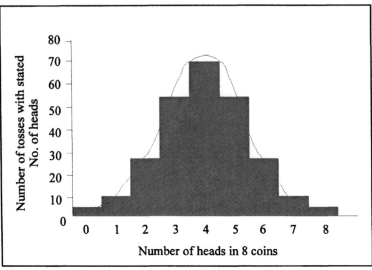

Figure 82

Comparing **Figure 81** with **Figure 82**, the distribution in **Figure 81** is skewed to the right whilst that of **Figure 82** is symmetrical. A histogram of a binomial distribution is symmetrical if, and only if, $p = q = 1/2$.

However when np is greater than 5 the histogram is reasonably symmetrical, but for values of np less than 5 the histogram will be noticeably skewed.

Example 5

It is known that a certain process produces 10% of defective articles. If a sample of 20 items is taken at random from a large batch of articles, find the probability of the sample containing two or more defective items.

Here $p = 0.1$ and $q = 0.9$. Since $n = 20$ we require the first two terms of the expansion of $(q + p)^{20}$.

Number of defective items in the sample	Term of the expansion	Probability of obtaining the stated number of defective items in the sample
1	q $20q^{19}p$	$(0.9)^{20}$ = 0.1216 $20 \times (0.9)^{19} \times (0.1)$ = 0.2702

$$\begin{array}{llllll} \text{Pr(less than 2)} & = & \text{Pr(0) + Pr(1)} & = & 0.1216 + 0.2702 & = & 0.3918 \\ \text{Pr(2 or more)} & = & \text{1 - Pr(less than 2)} & = & 1 - 0.3918 & = & 0.6082 \end{array}$$

(Since the total probability covering all possible events is 1).

The mean and standard deviation of a binomial distribution

Since the binomial distribution approximates to a normal distribution it may be used to construct a control chart for attributes based on the same principles as for variables. However, we need to know the statistics of the distribution.

It can be proved that the mean and standard deviation for a binomial distribution are given by:

$$\bar{x} = np \quad \text{and} \quad \sigma = \sqrt{npq}$$

Example 6

A production process is 6% defective. From a large batch a sample of 200 items is taken. Calculate the mean number of defectives in the sample and the standard deviation.

$$\bar{x} = np = 200 \times 0.06 = 12$$

$$\sigma = \sqrt{npq} = \sqrt{200 \times 0.06 \times 0.94} = 3.36$$

The Poisson Distribution

Introduction

A limitation of the binomial distribution is that it is necessary know the value of n the sample size. There are, however, many cases where the value of n is not known, for instance, in checking the number of weaving defects in a length of cloth or the number of welding defects in a welded assembly. Another distribution which provides us with a means of calculating probabilities is the Poisson distribution. It is based on the series for the natural number e^{17}. The Poisson distribution may be used to determine probabilities provided that λ is made equal to the average value of the occurrence of the event.

$$e^{\lambda} = 1 + \lambda + \frac{\lambda^2}{2!} + \frac{\lambda^3}{3!} + \ldots$$

In any calculations involving probabilities, the total probability covering all possible events must be equal to 1.

Now
$$e^{-\lambda} \times e^{\lambda} = e = 1$$

Hence, the product $e^{\lambda} \times e^{-\lambda}$ can be used to form a theoretical frequency distribution when it is written in the form:

$$e^{-\lambda}\left(1 + \lambda + \frac{\lambda^2}{2!} + \frac{\lambda^3}{3!} + \ldots\right)$$

Where each term represents the probability of 0, 1, 2, 3, 4 etc defectives given that the expected average number of defectives (np) is λ.

A distribution obtained by using this series is called a Poisson distribution. Tables of values of e^{-x} are available in most books of Mathematical Tables. Values are also easily

---

[17]   e is called a natural number since its occurrence, like π is found in the laws of many natural phenomena including electromagnetism. Its value is approximately 2.7183. It is also referred to as the exponential number.

found by entering a number in a scientific calculator and pressing the exponential key (often labelled e^x)

Example 1

A process is known to produce 2% of defective items. A sample of 100 items is drawn at random from a large batch of these items. Find the probabilities of obtaining 0, 1, 2, and 3 defective items in the sample.

Here $p = 0.02$ and $n = 100$

Hence $\lambda = np = 100 \times 0.02 = 2$

Using a calculator or referring to tables of e^{-x}, $e^{-2} = 0.1353$

Relation between the poisson and binomial distributions

In the binomial distribution if n (the number of items in a sample) is large and p (the fraction defective) is small then the event of finding a defective item in the sample is called a *rare event*.

In practice if $n \geq 50$ and $np < 5$ the event may be considered rare. In such cases the Poisson distribution gives a very close approximation to the binomial distribution.

Generally the approximation between a binomial and Poisson distribution is good if $p \leq 0.1$ and $np \leq 5$.

Using the poisson distribution as an approximation to the binomial distribution

In the majority of cases, the fraction defective, p, is usually small. If a sample of n items is taken from a batch of such items, the expected number of defectives in the sample will be $\lambda = np$. Hence the Poisson distribution may be used as an approximation to the binomial distribution if λ represents the expected number of defectives in a sample of n items.

Thus:

The probability of obtaining 0 defectives $\quad Pr(0) = e^{-\lambda} \times 1 = e^{-\lambda}$

The probability of obtaining 1 defective $\quad Pr(1) = e^{-\lambda} \times \lambda = \lambda e^{-\lambda}$

The probability of obtaining 2 defectives $\quad r(2) = e^{-\lambda} \times \dfrac{\lambda^2}{2!} = \dfrac{\lambda^2}{2!} e$

The probability of obtaining 3 defectives $\quad r(3) = e^{-\lambda} \times \dfrac{\lambda^3}{3!} = \dfrac{\lambda^3}{3!} e$

etc.

Number of defective items in the sample	Probability of obtaining the stated number of defective items in the sample
0	$Pr(0) = e^{-\lambda} = 0.1353$
1	$Pr(1) = \lambda e^{-\lambda} = \lambda\, Pr(0) = 2 \times 0.1353 = 0.2706$
2	$Pr(2) = \dfrac{\lambda^2}{2!} e^{-\lambda} = \dfrac{\lambda}{2} Pr(1) = \dfrac{2}{2} \times 0.2706 = 0.2706$
3	$Pr(3) = \dfrac{\lambda^3}{3!} e^{-\lambda} = \dfrac{\lambda}{3} Pr(2) = \dfrac{2}{3} \times 0.2706 = 0.1804$

Introduction to Quality Assurance

Example 2

It is known that a certain process produces 8% of defective items. A sample of 50 items is drawn from a large batch produced by the process. Find the probabilities of finding 0,1 and 2 defective items in the sample by using:

a)   the poisson distribution,
b)   the binomial distribution.

a)   For the poisson distribution $p = 0.08$ and $n = 50$

$$\therefore \quad \lambda \ = \ np \ = \ 50 \times 0.08 \ = \ 4$$
$$e^{-\lambda} \ = \ e^{-4} \ = \ 0.0183$$

b)   For the binomial distribution $p = 0.08$, $q = 0.92$ and $n = 50$

$$(q + p)^{50} = q^{50} + 50q^{49}p + \frac{50 \times 49}{2!} q^{48}p^2 \ ....$$
$$= q^{50} + 50q^{49}p + 1225q^{48}p^2 \ ....$$

Number Of Defectives In Sample	Probability	
	Poisson	**Binomial**
0	$e^{-\lambda}$ = 0.0183	$q^{50} = (0.92)^{50}$ = 0.0155
1	$\lambda\,e^{-\lambda}$ = 0.0732	$50q^{49}p$ = 0.0672
2	$\dfrac{\lambda^2}{2!} e^{-\lambda}$ = 0.1464	$1225q^{48}p^2$ = 0.1433

On comparing the probabilities as calculated for both the Poisson and binomial distributions, it will be seen that the Poisson distribution is a reasonable approximation to the binomial distribution.

Example 3

A process produces 3% of defective articles. From a large batch of these articles a sample of 80 items is taken. Find the probability that the sample will contain two or more defective items.

Here $p = 0.03$ and $n = 80$

Hence
$$\lambda = np = 80 \times 0.03 = 2.4$$
$$e^{-\lambda} = e^{-2.4} = 0.0907$$

Number of defective articles in the sample	Probability
0 1	$Pr(0) = e^{-\lambda} = 0.0907$ $Pr(1) = \lambda Pr(0) = 0.2177$

The Probability of 1 or less defective items in the sample
$$= 0.0907 + 0.2177 = 0.3084$$

Hence the probability of two or more defective items in the sample
$$= 1 - 0.3084 = 0.6916$$

Example 4

On checking several cartons containing large numbers of bolts, it was found that the average number of defective bolts in a carton was two. Find the probability of finding a box containing three or more defective bolts.

Here $\lambda = 2$ and $e^{-\lambda} = 0.1353$

Number of defective bolts in the carton	Probability		
0	$Pr(0) =$	$e^{-\lambda} = 0.1353$	
1	$Pr(1) =$	$\lambda Pr(0) = 0.2707$	
2	$Pr(2) =$	$\dfrac{\lambda}{2} Pr(1) = 0.2707$	

Probability of two or less defective bolts in a carton

$$= 0.1353 + 0.2707 + 0.2707 = 0.6767$$

Hence the probability of three or more defective bolts in a carton

$$= 1 - 0.6767 = 0.3233$$

It is likely, therefore, that 32.33% of all the cartons will contain three or more defective bolts.

Example 5

Twenty sheets of aluminium alloy were examined for surface flaws. The number of flaws per sheet were as follows:

Sheet number	0	1	2	3	4	5	6	7	8	9	10
Number of flaws	4	0	2	6	4	2	0	0	2	0	4

Sheet number	11	12	13	14	15	16	17	18	19	20
Number of flaws	4	2	1	3	4	1	1	5	3	2

Find the probability of finding a sheet, chosen at random from a batch of these sheets, which contains three or more surface flaws.

$$\lambda = \textit{the average number of flaws per sheet} = \frac{\textit{total number of flaws}}{\textit{number of sheets checked}}$$

$$= \frac{50}{20} = 2.5$$

$$e^{-\lambda} = e^{-2.5} = 0.0821$$

Number of flaws per sheet	Probability			
0	Pr(0) =	$e^{-\lambda}$		= 0.0821
1	Pr(1) =	$\lambda Pr(0)$		= 0.2052
2	Pr(2) =	$\dfrac{\lambda}{2} Pr(1)$		= 0.2565

Probability of finding a sheet with three or more surface flaws

= 1 - (0.0821 + 0.2052 + 0.2565) = 0.4562

Hence it is likely that 45.62% of the sheets in the batch will contain 3 or more surface flaws.

The mean and standard deviation of a poisson distribution

As with the binomial distribution it can be shown that the mean and standard deviation of a Poisson distribution are:

$$\bar{x} = \lambda \quad \text{and} \quad \sigma = \sqrt{\lambda}$$

Example 6

The following table shows the frequency of accidents in a factory during a 100 day period. Calculate the mean and standard deviation for this distribution. Show that the distribution is well represented by a Poisson distribution.

Number of accidents	0	1	2	3	4
Number of days on which this number of accidents occurred	42	36	14	6	2

Number of accidents = x	Frequency = f	fx	fx^2
0	42	0	0
1	36	36	36
2	14	28	56
3	6	18	54
4	2	8	32
	100	90	178

$$\bar{x} = \frac{90}{100} = 0.9 \qquad \sigma = \sqrt{\frac{178}{100} - (0.9)^2} = 0.985$$

Taking $\lambda = 0.9$, $\qquad e^{-\lambda} = 0.4066$

Number of accidents	Probability			Expected number of days = probability x 100
0	$\Pr(0) =$	$e^{-\lambda}$	$= 0.4066$	40.66 or 41
1	$\Pr(1) =$	$\lambda Pr(0)$	$= 0.3659$	36.59 or 37
2	$\Pr(2) =$	$\frac{\lambda}{2}Pr(1)$	$= 0.1647$	16.47 or 16
3	$\Pr(3) =$	$\frac{\lambda}{3}Pr(2)$	$= 0.0494$	4.94 or 5
4	$\Pr(4) =$	$\frac{\lambda}{4}Pr(3)$	$= 0.0111$	1.11 or 1

Hence the given distribution is well represented by a Poisson distribution with $\lambda = 0.9$. The standard deviation of the Poisson distribution is: $\sigma = \sqrt{\lambda} = \sqrt{0.9} = 0.949$ which agrees very well with the value calculated previously.

Implementing SQC

Introduction

Benefits of SQC:

- Monitoring a process by the use of control charts can provide the basis for a process improvement programme.
- Giving the operators the opportunity to use their abilities to the full in controlling and improving the process performance - (world class performance).
- Facilitating the process improvement for better quality, lower costs and greater productivity.
- SQC assists communication and discussion regarding the process performance, giving a better understanding of the requirements and processes ability to meet requirements.

Limitations of SQC: Although there are major benefits from the introduction of SQC, there can also be some limitations and problems.

The organisation may operate a piece work scheme which may prevent the operator having the time to complete the control chart. *One solution to this is for the inspector to complete the control chart. - This should be avoided at all costs as it defeats one of the main objectives of SQC - which is getting the operator involved with the quality of the work produced. The operator needs to be provided with all necessary facilities to perform SQC.*

The operator may not be capable of understanding or using SQC and may not wish to be involved. It isn't possible to gain appropriate commitment from all areas. *If SQC is properly explained then there will be no problems in understanding or gaining commitment. - It is only when the reasoning behind SQC is not fully explained that problems will be encountered.*

There will be certain expenditure associated with the introduction of SQC: resources to implement, equipment (measuring, chart holders and charts etc.), additional time completing and analysing the charts, - *but there are savings such as in quality, productivity etc.*

The process may not be capable of meeting the specification therefore, SQC cannot be applied. *Applying SQC will help identify the reasons for non-capability of the process and assist in establishing conformance to specification.*

Basic Statistical Methods

The process may have too many features that need control. *Failure Mode and Effects Analysis may assist in identifying the key features that need control. Alternatively, Multi-feature Attribute Charts could be employed.*

This is not applicable on certain processes, i.e. no measurements are taken, only pass or fail. *Attribute control charts can be used for go/nogo situations.*

Implementation consists of three key elements

STAGE 1:	Gather the data
STAGE 2:	Determine the control limits
STAGE 3:	Data analysis and variation reduction

These three stages are ceaselessly repeated for continuous improvement in process performance.

Variable Charts and Data

The procedure to be observed when SQC is applied to variable data is described below.

STAGE 1 Gather the data

Complete the process details on the Statistical Quality Control Chart (see **Figure 83** SQC Chart) using the Statistical Quality Control Chart and from the Process Capability Study determine an appropriate scale for the average x and range R.

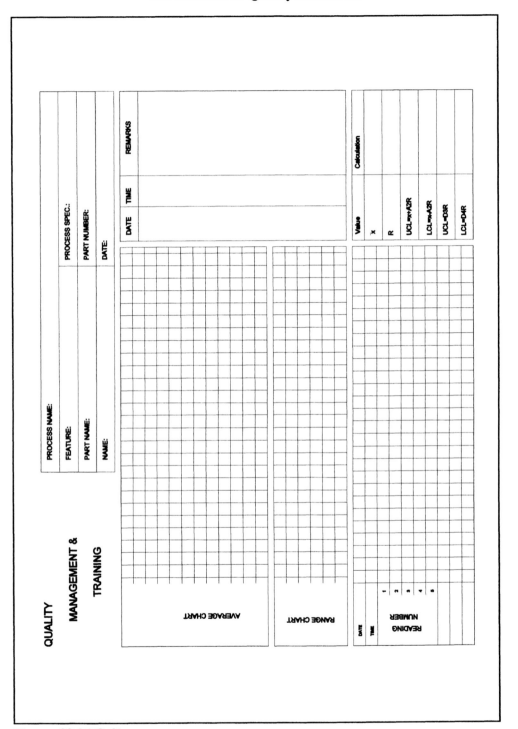

Figure 83 SQC Chart

For the average and range chart this can be approximately 2 * Process specification

Obtain first set of readings and record date, time and results. Circle or highlight any readings outside process specification.

Calculate average and range for each sample taken.

$$Average \ \bar{x} \ = \ \frac{\sum x_i}{n} \qquad (57)$$

Where Σx_i = the summation of each individual reading 1,2,3,...I
   n   = number of readings
 and R   = range, the difference between the highest and lowest value

Record x bar & R at the bottom of the chart

$$For \ the \ first \ example \ \bar{x} \ = \ \frac{51.7}{5} \ = \ 10.34$$
$$R \ = \ 10.4 \ - \ 10.3 \ = \ 0.1 \qquad (58)$$

See **Figure 84** Completed SPC Chart

Plot the value for average and range on the control chart directly above the date and time. Join the points together with a straight line.

Now repeat this exercise until approximately 25 samples or 100 readings have been obtained.

STAGE 2 Determine the control limits

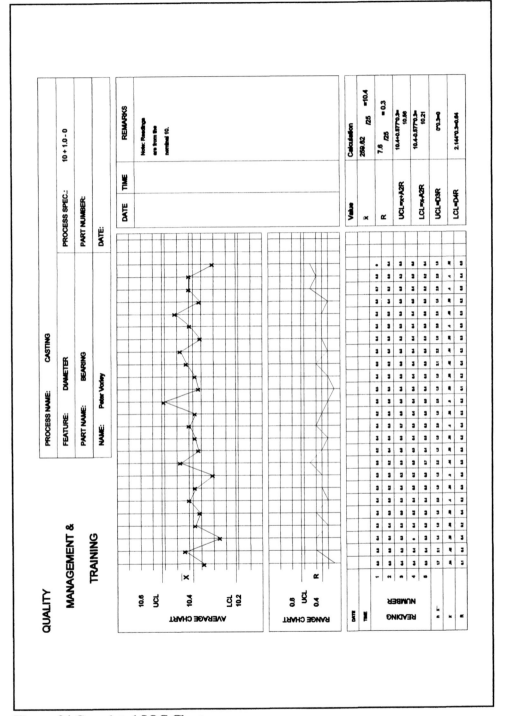

Figure 84 Completed SQC Chart

Calculate the average range value R.

$$\overline{R} = \frac{\sum R_i}{k}$$ (59)

Where $\sum R_i$ = the summation of each range value
and k = the number of samples taken

$$\overline{R} = \frac{7.6}{25} = 0.304$$ (60)

Draw $\overline{R}$ on the range chart as a thick line

Calculate the control limits for the range chart.

The control limits are used as a guide to determine process performance. The use of the control limits is described in the section - STAGE 3 Data Analysis and Variation Reduction.

In order to calculate the control limits, it is necessary to use certain constants. In Table - Control Limit Constants for each sample size n are given constants A_2, D_3 and D_4 which are used in the control limit calculations.

The first constant to be used is D_4 which can be found in Table - Control Limit

Table - Control Limited Constants

n	2	3	4	5	6	7	8	9	10
A_2	1.880	1.023	0.729	0.577	0.483	0.419	0.373	0.337	0.308
D_3	0	0	0	0	0	0.076	0.136	0.184	0.223
D_4	3.268	2.574	2.282	2.114	2.004	1.924	1.864	1.816	1.777

Constants by locating on row 'n' the sample size and read off the value for D_4. Record the value of D_4.

Calculate Upper Control Limit for ranges.

where $UCL_R = D_4*R$

In the example $UCL_R = 2.114*0.304 = 0.642$

Draw UCL_R on the range chart as a thick line.

Calculate the Lower Control Limit for ranges.

$$LCL_R = D_3*R$$

D_3 is given in Table - Control Limit Constants and is found in a similar way to D_4.

In the example $LCL_R = 0*0.304 = 0$

Draw LCL_R on the range chart as a thick line.

Calculate the process average.

$$Average\ \overline{\overline{x}} = \frac{\sum xi}{k} \qquad\qquad (61)$$

Where $\sum xi$ = the summation of each individual sample average

$$In\ the\ example\ (Completed\ SQC\ Chart)\ \overline{\overline{x}} = \frac{259.62}{25} = 10.38 \qquad (62)$$

Draw x bar on the average chart as a thick line

Calculate the control limit for average charts.

Determine the value for A_2, where A_2 is given in the table; it is found in a similar way to D_4.

Basic Statistical Methods

Calculate Upper Control Limit for averages

$$UCL_x = \bar{x} + (A_2 * R) \tag{63}$$

In the example (Completed SQC Chart) $UCL_x = 10.38 + (0.577*0.304)$

Draw UCL_x on the average chart as a thick line

Calculate the Lower Control Limit for averages

$$LCL_x = \bar{x} - (A_2 * R) \tag{64}$$

In the example (Completed SQC Chart) $LCL_x = 10.38 - (0.577*0.304)$

Draw LCL_x on the average chart as a thick line

STAGE 3 Data analysis and variation reduction

One of the key purposes of using control charts is to improve quality by reducing variation. Consequently techniques need to be employed which can help identify any sources of variation. One such method is to identify the presence of non-random effects and, if possible, eliminate them. Non-random effects can be recognised by applying the following tests when examining the charts.

TEST 1   **Any point outside the control limit**

TEST 2   **A series of seven points above or below the average**

TEST 3   **A trend of seven points in a consistent direction from the mean**

TEST 4   **Any other cyclic pattern**

Once a non-random effect has been identified, its source should be investigated to determine what action is necessary to (a) correct the non-conformity and (b) prevent it recurring. As an aid to trouble shooting when non-random variations occur, it is important to keep a log of any changes such as re-setting, change of shift, material or equipment changes.

TEST 1

Points outside the control limits. The control limits have been calculated using the constants (A_2, D_3 and D_4). These constants are calculated so that there is only a one in a 1000 chance of points lying outside the Control Limits. It is reasonable, therefore, to presume that a non-random effect has caused the change.

A point outside the control limit (either above or below) could indicate that:

- The point has been wrongly plotted
- The control limit has been incorrectly calculated or plotted
- The process has worsened or improved
- The inspection standard has changed

TEST 2

A series of seven points above or below the average. A change in the process average could indicate that the average has moved and stabilised at a new higher or lower level.

Basic Statistical Methods

A run of seven points above the average could indicate that, on the average chart, the accuracy or process average has worsened. On the average chart, - a run of seven points below the average could indicate that the accuracy or process average has improved.

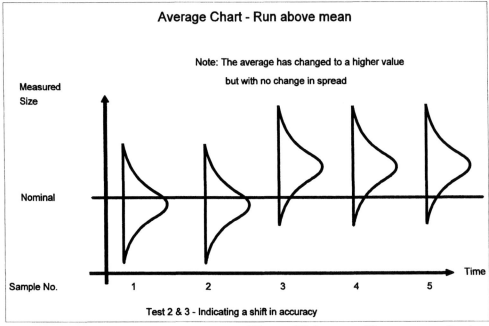

Figure 85 Average Chart - a run of points

The effect on the process distribution is shown in the diagram **Figure 85**. The spread of the process has not changed but the setting has undergone a change, resulting in a shifted average and stabilising at a new higher level.

On the range chart, - a run of seven points above the average would indicate the repeatability or spread of the process has worsened, or the inspection standard or measuring system has changed.

On the range chart, - a run of seven points below the average would indicate that the repeatability or spread has improved, or the inspection standard or measuring system has changed.

270

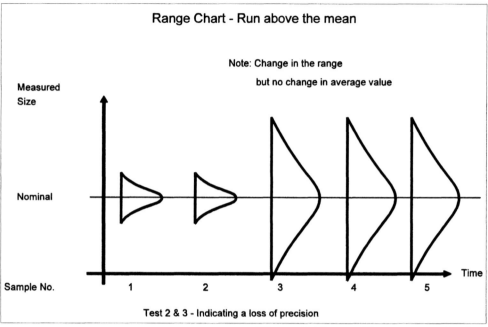

Figure 86 Range Chart - a run of points

The effect on the process spread of a run of points above the average on the range chart is represented in the diagram **Figure 86**. The location of the spread has not changed but the width of the spread has increased. Consequently, there will be greater variation between the individual process values.

TEST 3

Any trends within the control limits (even when all points are within the control limits) should be investigated as it may be an indication of conditions which, if ignored, could lead to the process moving outside the control limits, or an improvement opportunity that should be encouraged.

Trends - on the average chart.

A run of seven points where each point is higher or lower than the previous may indicate that the accuracy or process average is changing, possibly worsening. The inspection standard or measuring system could be changing.

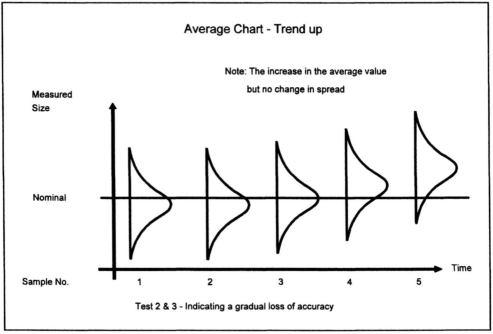

Average Chart - Trend up

Note: The increase in the average value but no change in spread

Measured Size

Nominal

Sample No.   1   2   3   4   5

Time

Test 2 & 3 - Indicating a gradual loss of accuracy

Figure 87 Average Chart - Trend

The diagram **Figure 87** represents the effect on the process distribution as a result of a run of points on the average chart. There is no change in the process spread but a shift upwards of the process setting or location.

Trends - on the Range Chart.

A run of seven points where each point is higher than the previous could indicate that the repeatability or spread has worsened and is still deteriorating. A run of seven points where each point is lower than the previous could indicate that, the repeatability or spread has improved and is still improving so investigate and encourage this trend.

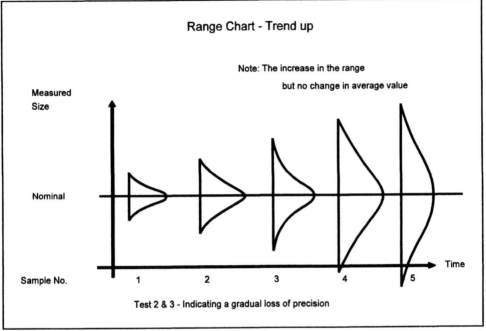

Figure 88 Range Chart - Trend

The diagram **Figure 88** represents the changes to the process distribution as a consequence of a run upwards of points on the range chart. The spread of the distribution is deteriorating and there will be a steadily worsening variation between individual process values.

TEST 4

The control limits are such that approximately 2/3 of the data points should lie within the middle third region of the control limits. About 1/3 of the data points should lie in the outer two thirds of the control limits.

Cyclic patterns may be due to plotting points from samples taken from different conditions e.g. different processes, different shifts, different batches.

Variation reduction

Identify and remedy: Once a non-random cause of variation has been investigated and remedied, the process should have improved. If subsequent data points are consistently

273

below the previous average (confirming the improvement) then the control limits can be re-calculated for the new improved process performance.

Continuous process improvement: The data should continue to be collected, plotted on the chart and analysed to identify further process improvements. It may be appropriate to use the techniques detailed in the section on Total Quality Management to assist in achieving process improvements, particularly Pareto analysis and cause and effect diagrams.

Attribute charts and data

The previous section described the procedure to be observed when SQC is applied to variable data. This section shows how to apply SQC when attribute data is collected.

The data will need to be divided into samples or sub-groups of 'n' items. The number of items in each sample should preferably remain constant (although this is not essential). The interval between each sample should be chosen on the basis of production frequency, the importance of the operation or process. The samples need to be sufficiently large to allow defectives to appear (although hopefully none). The samples should be taken from one process otherwise it will be difficult to identify the source or cause of any defectives. I.e. separate charts should be kept for different processes.

STAGE 1 Gather the data

Decide on a sample size in accordance with the above rules.
Record the number of defects/defectives in each sample. See **Figure 89**.

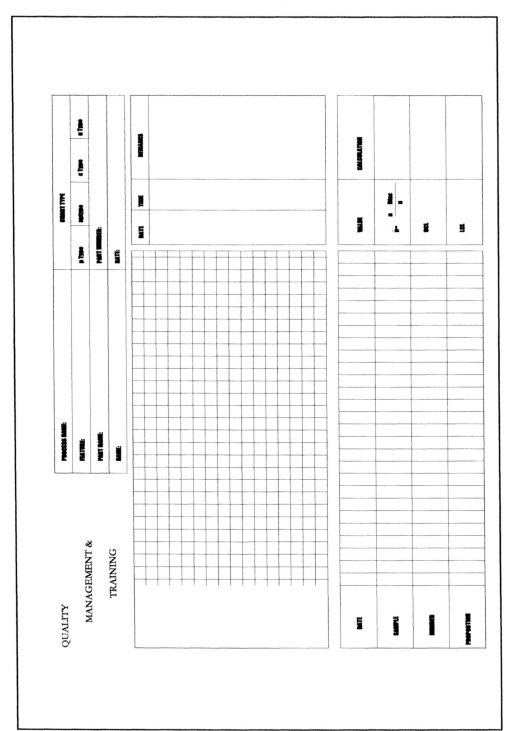

Figure 89 SQC Chart for Attributes

The proportion or number of defects/defectives on the vertical axis and the sample identification (hour, day etc.) on the horizontal axis. The vertical axis should extend from zero to about 1.5 times the highest point expected.

Depending on the chart type selected, plot the value of p, np, c or u for each sample on the chart.

STAGE 2 Determine the control limits

(I) The p chart for PROPORTION OF DEFECTIVES (NON-CONFORMING UNITS)

The proportion of defectives is p i.e. the number of defectives (np) divided by the number in the sample.

$$p = \frac{np}{n} \tag{65}$$

Calculate the average number of defectives for the process

$$p = \frac{Total\ number\ defectives}{Total\ number\ inspected} \tag{66}$$

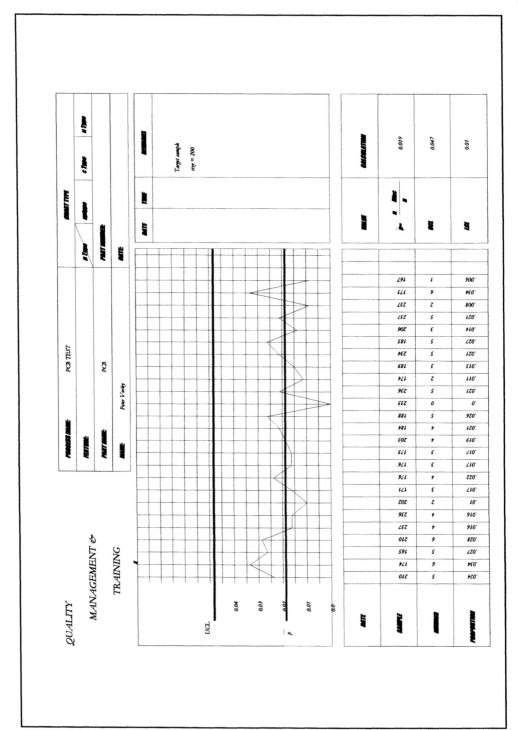

Figure 90 Completed SQC Chart for Attributes

Calculate the Control Limits (UCL, LCL).

$$UCL_p = \bar{p} + 3 * \sqrt{\frac{\bar{p}(1-\bar{p})}{\bar{n}}} \qquad (67)$$

$$LCL_p = \bar{p} - 3 * \sqrt{\frac{\bar{p}(1-\bar{p})}{\bar{n}}} \qquad (68)$$

Draw the process mean (p bar) and control limits on the chart and label (p, UCL_p and LCL_p).

Note 1:
As the sample size can vary with p charts then this can affect the control limits. Therefore, it may be necessary to recalculate the control limits. Once calculated the new control limits should be plotted on the control charts.

Note 2:
If the LCL is negative then ignore this control limit since it is not possible to have less than zero defectives. (See **Figure 90** Completed SQC Chart for Attributes).

ii) The np chart for NUMBER OF DEFECTIVES

The number of defectives is np i.e. the number in the sample multiplied by the proportion of defectives in the sample.

Calculate the average number of defectives for the process

$$\bar{np} = \frac{np_1 + np_2 + np_3 + ...np_n}{m} \qquad (69)$$

Where np_1, np_2 etc. are the number of defectives in each of m samples inspected.

Calculate the Control Limits (UCL, LCL).

$$UCL_{np} = \overline{np} + 3 * \sqrt{\frac{\overline{np}(1 - \overline{np})}{\overline{n}}} \qquad (70)$$

$$LCL_{np} = \overline{np} - 3 * \sqrt{\frac{\overline{np}(1 - \overline{np})}{\overline{n}}} \qquad (71)$$

Draw the process mean and control limits on the chart and label (np, UCL_{np} and LCL_{np}).

Note:
If the LCL is negative ignore this control limit since it is not possible to have less than zero defects.

iii) The c chart for NUMBER OF DEFECTS (NON-CONFORMITIES)

The number of defects is c.

Calculate the average number of defects for the process

$$\overline{c} = \frac{c_1 + c_2 + c_3 + \dots c_m}{m} \qquad (72)$$

Where c_1, c_2 etc. are the number of defects in each of m samples inspected.

Calculate the Control Limits (UCL, LCL).

$$UCL_c = \overline{c} + 3 * \sqrt{\overline{c}} \qquad (73)$$

$$LCL_c = \bar{c} - (3 * \sqrt{\bar{c}}$$ (74)

Draw the process mean and control limits on the chart and label (c, UCL_c and LCL_c).

Note: If the LCL is negative ignore this control limit since it is not possible to have less than zero defectives.

iv) The u chart for NUMBER OF DEFECTS (NON-CONFORMITIES) per unit

The number of defects per unit is u.

Calculate the average number of defects per unit for the process

$$\bar{u} = \frac{u_1 + u_2 + u_3 + \ldots u_m}{n_1 + n_2 + n_3 + \ldots n_m}$$ (75)

Where u_1, u_2 etc. are the number of defects per unit in each of m samples inspected.

Calculate the Control Limits (UCL, LCL).

$$UCL_u = \bar{u} + 3 * \sqrt{\frac{\bar{u}}{n}}$$ (76)

$$LCL_u = \bar{u} - 3 * \sqrt{\frac{\bar{u}}{n}}$$ (77)

Draw the process mean and control limits on the chart and label (u, UCL_u and LCL_u).

Note 1:

As the sample size can vary with u charts then this can affect the control limits. Therefore, it may be necessary to recalculate the control limits with the new sample size varies. Once calculated, the new control limits should be plotted on the control charts.

Note 2:

If the LCL is negative then ignore this control limit since it is not possible to have less than zero defectives.

Multiple characteristic charts

With any of the above p, np, c and u charts, it is only possible to monitor one characteristic. With all of these charts (p, np, c, and u) it may on occasion be necessary to monitor more than one characteristic or feature. In this situation, a multiple characteristic chart can be employed which enables several characteristics to be recorded on the one chart. Thus giving a more comprehensive picture of the process performance and assisting with identifying the causes of variation. (See **Figure 91** Attribute Control Chart - Multiple Features). Note that a Pareto Analysis of the various characteristics can be performed on the data calculated on the right-hand side of the chart.

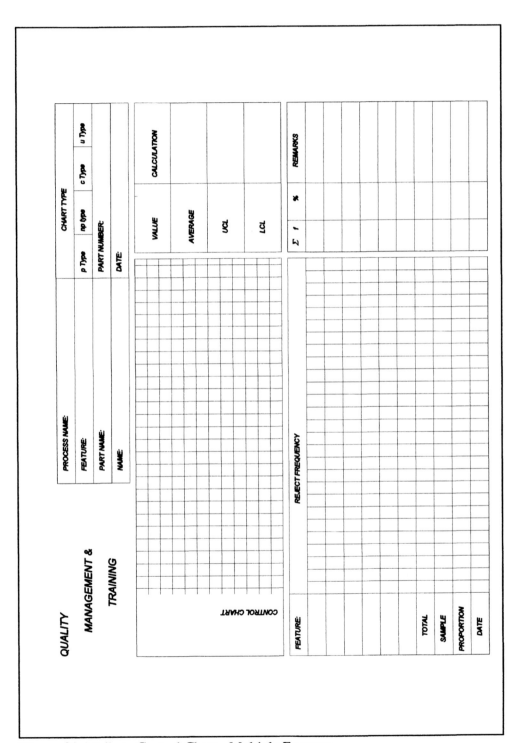

Figure 91 Attribute Control Chart - Multiple Features

Statistical Tolerancing

Introduction

Precision is cost related. Tighter tolerances usually mean higher costs. Statistical Tolerancing is a method of avoiding specifying unnecessarily tight tolerances. When assemblies consist of several mating components the designer will usually select tolerances for the individual components that will make tolerance clashes impossible. This is an understandable decision as it avoids any problems in assembling the finished product. However, in practice the designer is worrying unnecessarily because the chance of such a tolerance clash condition actually occurring is very remote. This is because statistically, the sum of the tolerances is unlikely to be equal to the arithmetical sum. This is due to the fact that, given that the component sizes are normally distributed, the chances of every component in the assembly being at one extreme limit is very remote.

Consider the following example.

Figure 92 shows a bracket which contains 10 laminations. The 10 laminations fit inside a bracket with a 20/20.1mm gap. If the designer uses

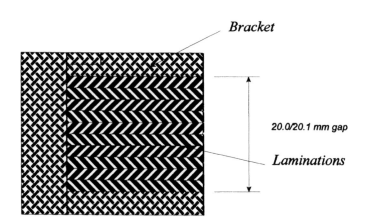

Figure 92 Lamination

arithmetical tolerances then the following equation would apply.

$$\frac{Total\ tolerance}{Number\ of\ Components} = Component\ Tolerance = \frac{0.1}{10} = 0.01mm \qquad (78)$$

In effect this means that each lamination must be between 2.00 to 2.01mm in size. Such a tolerance would only be necessary if all laminations were at one extreme which is a very unlikely event.

Introduction to Quality Assurance

Statistical tolerancing takes into consideration that this is a very unlikely event. If statistical tolerancing was applied to this example then the tolerance could be much greater.

From the section on Process Capability Studies, it was suggested that for process capability the process specification should be equal to or greater than six standard deviations.

It can be shown that the total variance equals the sum of the individual variance.

$$\sigma_t^2 = \sigma_1^2 + \sigma_2^2 + \sigma_3^2 + \sigma_4^2 + \ldots \ldots \ldots \sigma_n^2$$

Where $\sigma_1^2, \sigma_2^2, \sigma_3^2, \sigma_4^2, \ldots \ldots \ldots \sigma_n^2$

are the individual standard deviations of each component

and σ_t is the total standard deviation   **(79)**

Now if the tolerance = 6σ then we can substitute T for σ thus:

$$T_t^2 = T_1^2 + T_2^2 + T_3^2 + T_4^2 + \ldots \ldots \ldots T_n^2 \qquad \textbf{(80)}$$

Where the individual tolerances are equal then this reduces to:

$$T_t^2 = T_i^2 * n$$

$$or \; T_i = T_t * \sqrt{\frac{1}{n}}$$

Where   **(81)**

T_i = *The individual tolerance*
T_t = *The total tolerance*
n = *The number of items*

Basic Statistical Methods

For the lamination example, the tolerance for each individual lamination is:

$$T_i = 0.1 * \sqrt{\frac{1}{10}} = 0.032mm \tag{82}$$

This tolerance (0.032mm) is obviously an improvement on the 0.01mm which was given by arithmetical tolerancing. Statistical tolerancing can provide cost and time savings. In the example the tolerance is now over three times larger, with probably no effect on the overall assembly performance.

Assumptions for statistical tolerancing to be viable

The process needs to be capable, the process distribution needs to be normal, and vary equally around the mean. The components must be randomly selected. If these criteria are not met then these principles may not apply.

Following are some other examples of the application of statistical tolerancing.

The first example is of a hole and shaft. The clearance between the hole and the shaft needs to be 0.01 to 0.05mm. Sharing the arithmetical tolerance equally between the hole and shaft would mean that the hole and shaft tolerance would be 0.02mm each.

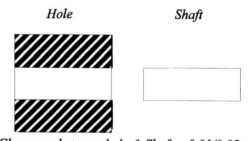

Clearance between hole & Shaft = 0.01/0.05mm

Figure 93

However, if the statistical tolerancing equation is used then the tolerance becomes 0.028mm.

$$Individual\ tolerance\ T_i = 0.04 * \sqrt{\frac{1}{2}} = 0.028mm \tag{83}$$

The second example is where a complete bar length is made up of three individual bars of various length and tolerance.

Bar length

Figure 94

The arithmetical variation in bar length will be 0.2+0.4+0.8 = 1.4mm

The statistical variation in bar length will be:

$$T_t^2 = 0.2^2 + 0.4^2 + 0.8^2$$
$$T_t = 0.92mm \qquad\qquad (84)$$

As previously explained, there are benefits to be gained from the use of statistical tolerancing but there are also dangers. It is important that the process is confirmed to be capable, otherwise the calculation may be in error.

287

Cusum Charts

Introduction

With a standard quality control chart, action is dependent upon individually plotted points. Although some trends may be detectable, generally no action will be taken so long as points lie within the control limits. Hence a run of points above or below the average may go unnoticed because the position of each point is independent of those which preceded it. This may be unsatisfactory as it could be that the average value over a period is the important factor, rather than individual values.

The technique which uses all available information and is more sensitive to short and long term changes and trends, even small but persistent changes, is the *Cumulative Sum Chart*, or *CUSUM* as it is called. This type of chart was developed in Britain in the 1950's and is one of the most powerful management tools available for the detection of trends and slight changes in data.

The Cusum chart is, therefore, a much more sensitive device in detecting changes in average value than normal charting procedures.

The Cusum chart has application in many fields of management control not only quality control. Other areas include:

forecasting   -   actual v forecasted sales
absenteeism   -   detection of slight changes
production levels   -   detection of slight changes
plant breakdown   -   maintenance performance

and many others in which an indication of change is required.

Case Study 1

Suppose a liquid chemical were to be prepared, in which the average content of a particular ingredient needed to be as near as possible to 10 g/litre. The liquid produced will be mixed in bulk before the next operation, so minor variations do not matter, so long as the average is kept at 10 g. A cumulative sum chart may be used for this. Start with a reference value, in this case the 10 g/litre, as the basis for controlling the process. This may well be the previous average performance of the process. The process is tested by sampling at intervals The different between the observed sample values and the target reference value is added to the previous value and plotted.

Introduction to Quality Assurance

Suppose that the first 10 results are:

Observation No.	Observed Value = 0	Deviation from Target (10)	Cumulative Sum of Deviations
1	10	0	0
2	11	+1	+1
3	9	-1	0
4	10	0	0
5	12	+2	+2
6	9	-1	+1
7	10	0	+1
8	8	-2	-1
9	10	0	-1
10	11	+1	0
	Average = 10		

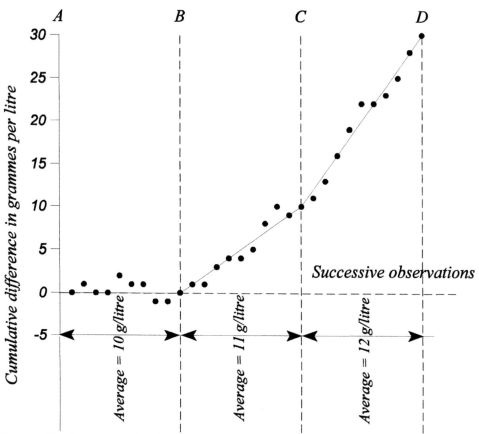

Figure 95   Example of a CUSUM chart

These results are plotted in section AB of **Figure 95**

Suppose the observations continue as follows.

Observation No.	Observed Value = 0	Deviation from Target (10)	Cumulative Sum of Deviations
11	11	+1	+1
12	10	0	+1
13	12	+2	+3
14	11	+1	+4
15	10	0	+4
16	11	+1	+5
17	13	+3	+8
18	12	+2	+10
19	9	-1	+9
20	11	+1	+10
	Average = 11		

These results plotted in section BC of **Figure 95** form a straight line going upwards is produced and this indicates that the process has changed to a new average level which is higher than the reference value. A check shows that it is averaging 11 g/litre instead of 10. In section CD of **Figure 95** further observations are plotted, in which the average is 12 g/litre.

Interpretation of a Cusum chart is therefore as follows:

1. A horizontal line of points means that the process is holding an average value equal to the reference value.

2. A straight line upwards means that the process has changed to a new steady average level, which is above the reference value. The steeper the line, the greater the difference between the new average and the reference value. (Conversely if the straight line is downwards, the new average is below the reference value.)

Basic Statistical Methods

3. If the line is curved upwards, the new average is above the reference and still increasing. Similarly, if it is curved downwards, the average is below the reference and still reducing.

4. Notice that the position of a point on the chart represents the cumulative past history of the process since observations were started. Thus there is no particular significance in whether the point is high up or low down on the paper. If points run out of the top of the chart, it is common practice to restart them again near the bottom. All that matters is the direction in which the points are heading. In the above example, the process must be adjusted so that they keep a horizontal course.

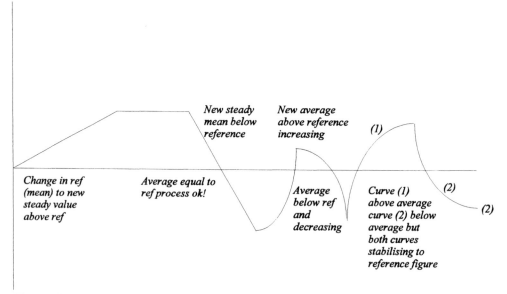

Figure 96

Introduction to Quality Assurance

Scope and General Principles

Scope. This section introduces the principles of Cusum techniques and includes the preparation, charting, presentation and interpretation of data, with worked examples.

Fundamental requirements. The fundamental requirements for Cusum charting are as follows:

  a. The observations should be at least on an interval scale of measurement.
  b. There should be logical grounds for their being sorted into a sequence for plotting.

These requirements are taken in order. The interval properly requires any given numerical difference between two observations to have the same interpretation throughout the range of the variable. Thus a difference of 0.1 mm between the lengths of two objects has the same meaning whether the objects are woodscrews of length 10.1 mm and 10.0 mm or steel girders of length 10,000.1 mm and 10,000.0 mm although the latter difference may be unimportant. Many arbitrary scales do not have this properly: defect ratings are an example, where perhaps a serious defect scores 10 points, a moderate defect 5 and a minor defect 1. We cannot then interpret this to meant that the following items are necessarily equally undesirable, although their differences are zero:

Item A	One serious defect	Score = 10
Item B	Two serious defects	Score = 10
Item C	One moderate, five minor defects	Score = 10
Item D	Ten serious defects	Score = 10

Interpretation of 'average' score could be misleading if the balance of major, moderate and minor defects, rather than merely their overall frequency, changes.

The logical sequences property may arise in numerous ways. Most obviously, the observations may occur in a time or length sequence, thus forming a natural progression. Monitoring for quality or process control provides many cases of this kind.

Basic Statistical Methods

Secondly, conditions in the environment from which the observations are taken may vary either deliberately or fortuitously. The data thus falls into obvious groups, but the ordering or observations within these groups may not be of any particular importance.

Thirdly, the items themselves may provide a basis for ordering or, more commonly, for grouping. Manufactured components may be segregated according to the identity of the machine from which they are sampled, or on the basis of whether or not they possess specified defects or other attributes.

Fourthly, observations may be ordered according to the value of some auxiliary variable measured on the items, the Cusum then providing a means of presenting or investigating relationships between variables, augmenting a regression or correlation analysis.

This list of possibilities is not exhaustive and any kind of ordering or grouping that uses some structural feature of the observations or the background from which they are taken may provide the basis for the Cusum sequences.

Types of data amendable to Cusum charting. Many types of data satisfy the fundamental requirements (a) and (b) and some examples may be useful. Perhaps the most frequent applications of Cusum charts have been in quality control, where observations (e.g. sample means or ranges) are plotted in sequence to provide a continuous assessment of the state of a process. It is sometimes assumed that such observations have to be normally distributed for the application of Cusum charts. This is not the case, although some distribution models may be necessary when setting up the decision rules. However, when using a Cusum chart as a device for effective data presentation, it is not necessary to specify a distribution, nor to require independence between successive observations (again, this condition is important for decision rules, but not for data presentation). Indeed, the Cusum chart may assist in the identification of features such as serial correlation or cyclic behaviour.

Thus data involving ranges or samples estimates of standard deviation may be plotted on Cusum charts, as well as sample averages. Counts of defects or defectives are also encountered in quality control and may be monitored by Cusum charts.

Introduction to Quality Assurance

Outside the quality control area, many applications arise. The consumption of fuel by transport vehicles even by private cars, the response of patients to changes in treatment, trials of systems or weapons in which each trial has a success of failure (1 or 0) outcome: all provide data amenable to Cusum charting.

Some forms of indirect data also occur. In setting up a forecasting system, its performance may be monitored by comparing predicted values with actual values when they become available. The validity or adequacy of a mathematical model for an experiment may be assessed by a Cusum of the residual errors. In this instance the various levels of experimental factors will provide the basis for grouping or ordering.

Data in the commercial and administrative areas may also be usefully subjected to Cusum analysis. Monitoring of absence rates and examination for day-of-the-week patterns, auditing of frequency of card-punch errors, assessment of labour turnover, are typical examples. Even where the size of the sample or group, for which such rates are calculated varies, the Cusum chart can be simply modified to accommodate this.

Purpose of Cusum charting. Cusum charting has two main purposes, which are related to the way in which the data is collected.

1. *Monitoring or control.* Values are plotted on the Cusum chart as they occur, with the aim of detecting any change in the nature of the process generating the observations, such as a change in mean or variability.

   Decision rules are necessary to rationalise interpretation of the chart. When an appropriate decision rule so indicates, some action is taken, depending on the nature of the process. Typical actions are, as follows:

   i.   In a quality control application, adjustment of the process conditions;
   ii.   In a more general technical context, investigation of the underlying cause of the change;
   iii.   In monitoring the behaviour of a forecasting system, analysis of and, if necessary, modification to the model or its parameters.

2. *Data analysis.* A complete set of observations is subjected to Cusum analysis, the object being to detect whether changes (e.g. in mean level) have occurred at one or more points in time, or between the rational groups into which the data are divided. The objectives are close to those of hypothesis testing, except that the group or time-segments into which the data are divided may be based on an examination of the Cusum pattern, instead of being determined in advance as in conventional

hypothesis testing. In essence it is an attempt to detect any changed points in the sequence.

Where historical data, i.e. data collected over time, and measuring the past behaviour of systems are involved, the procedure is often termed 'retrospective' or 'post mortem' analysis. However, as previously noted, grouping by features other than time may often be appropriate.

For either primary purpose, or in intermediate cases, the changes should be assessed against the intrinsic variations in the data. For time sequences, this means detecting sustained changes in a typical level against a suitable measure of short-term variation. For other forms of grouping, the problem, such as in analysis of variance, is in comparing between-group variation with the variation within groups.

Scaling factors with cusum charts

The main interest is in the slope of a Cusum plot, the choice of its vertical and horizontal scales will be very important. It can be quite useful to have templates which indicate the expected slope for various quality levels. This may be in the form of attributes or variables as illustrated below.

A example of Cusum charting from lithographic plate process.

For Attributes

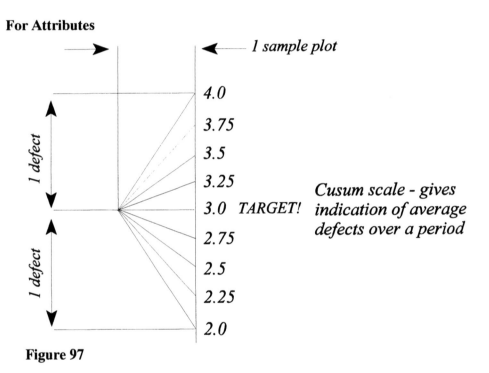

1 sample plot

4.0

3.75

3.5

3.25

3.0 TARGET!

2.75

2.5

2.25

2.0

Cusum scale - gives indication of average defects over a period

1 defect

1 defect

Figure 97

Scaling for variable Cusum charts

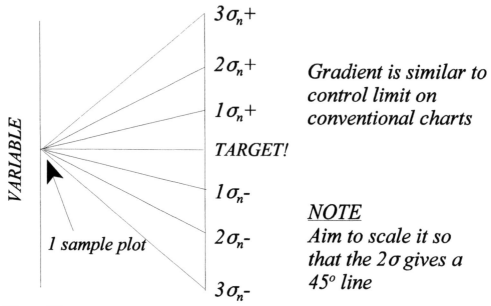

Gradient is similar to control limit on conventional charts

Figure 98

<u>*NOTE*</u>
Aim to scale it so that the 2σ gives a $45°$ line

Transparent overlay

Figure 99 V-Mask for Cusum chart

Point A is placed on the last considered point. If the plotted points fall within the Vee, then the process may be assumed to be under statistical control.

Index

Index

Index